Voices of Change

Voices of Change
Short Stories by Saudi Arabian Women Writers

edited and translated by

Abubaker Bagader
Ava M. Heinrichsdorff
Deborah S. Akers

additional translations by Abdul-Aziz Al-Sebail

LYNNE
RIENNER
PUBLISHERS

BOULDER
LONDON

Published in the United States of America in 1998 by
Lynne Rienner Publishers, Inc.
1800 30th Street, Boulder, Colorado 80301

and in the United Kingdom by
Lynne Rienner Publishers, Inc.
3 Henrietta Street, Covent Garden, London WC2E 8LU

© 1998 by Lynne Rienner Publishers, Inc. All rights reserved

Library of Congress Cataloging-in-Publication Data
Voices of change : short stories by Saudi Arabian women writers /
  edited and translated by Abubaker Bagader, Ava M. Heinrichsdorff,
  Deborah S. Akers.
    ISBN 978-1-55587-750-7 (hc : alk. paper).
    ISBN 978-1-55587-775-0 (pbk. : alk. paper)
      1. Short stories, Arabic—Saudi Arabia—Translations into English.
    2. Arabic fiction—Women authors—Translations into English.
    3. Arabic fiction—20th century—Translations into English.
    I. Bagader, Abu Bakr.   II. Heinrichsdorff, Ava Molnar.   III. Akers,
    Deborah S., 1955–   .
    PJ8005.8.V65   1997
    892'.7301089287'09045—dc21   97-26942
                                                                            CIP

British Cataloguing in Publication Data
A Cataloguing in Publication record for this book
is available from the British Library.

Printed and bound in the United States of America

 The paper used in this publication meets the requirements
of the American National Standard for Permanence of
Paper for Printed Library Materials Z39.48–1992.

10 9 8 7 6 5 4

*In memory of Jihan and Loulou,
who spoke from the heart*

Contents

Preface	ix
Introduction	
Abubaker Bagader, Ava M. Heinrichsdorff, and Deborah S. Akers	1

Part One   Life Passages

Had I Been Male	
Najat Khayyat	19
School Diaries	
Badriyyah al-Bishir	23
Tears of Joy and Sorrow	
Jamilah Fatani	29
Why Shouldn't I Be Like Her?	
Jamilah Fatani	35
Zainab	
Sharifah ash-Shamlan	39
The Duties of a Working Wife	
Wafa Munawwar	43
Complete Calm	
Sharifah ash-Shamlan	47
To Celebrate Being a Woman	
Fatimah al-ᶜUtaybi	53
The Dove Is a Woman	
Nurah al-Ghamdi	57
Just Give Me the Right to Dream	
Fatimah al-ᶜUtaybi	63

Part Two   Social Issues

The Loss	
Khayriyyah as-Saqqaf	69

Saffron
  Fatimah ad-Dawsari 73
Wednesday Night
  Badriyyah al-Bishir 77
In a Puzzling Whirlwind
  Amal cAbdul-Hamid 83
The Reflection
  Khayriyyah as-Saqqaf 87

Part Three   Love: Romantic, Requited, and Otherwise

I Will Not Return
  Qumashah al-cUlayyan 95
If Only It Were Pity
  Lamia Baeshen 101
Fall Nights
  Samirah Khashuqji 107
A Single-Winged Bird
  Lamia Baeshen 113
The Last Dream
  Mona A. Al-Dokair 119
The Game
  Sarah Buhaymid 127
I Never Lied
  Qumashah al-cUlayyan 131
Take Me with You
  Najat Khayyat 135

Part Four   Memories

Burqan's Ghost
  Nurah al-Ghamdi 141
The Madman
  Jamilah Fatani 149
One Thousand Braids and a Governess
  Raja' cAlim 155

Glossary 163
About the Authors 167
About the Book and Editors 171

Preface

Our purpose for putting this volume together was to give Saudi Arabian women a voice in the English-speaking world. Since our book is the first of its kind, we had no models to rely upon. The process of elimination from an extensive group of works was our first challenge. One priority was to ensure that stories by women from the major regions of the Saudi Kingdom were represented. We also required that each of the stories fulfill at least one of three criteria: tell the story well, make a social point, or be a well-known work by a significant author. Although the stories are neither representative of Saudi literature nor comprehensive, we feel that they do reflect the major concerns of contemporary Saudi women.

As the translators and editors of such a collection, we are appropriately multicultural: male/female, Saudi/American/European, and sociologist/anthropologist/writer. Abubaker Bagader, a sociologist based in Jeddah, collected dozens of prospective stories from local sources; Ava Heinrichsdorff, a fiction writer herself, and Deborah Akers, an anthropologist, brought to the project their Western perspectives and complementary skills, helping to select those stories that spoke best to Western audiences.

Our endeavor forced us to consider new points of view about Arab women and the art of storytelling. In our collaboration we discovered that when multiple perspectives and voices converge, it is possible for real understanding to occur. We hope that readers will have a similar experience and that the collection will help break down Western stereotypes about Saudi women as passive, submissive, and unintelligent. When allowed to speak for themselves, these women are assertive and critical beings who command respect.

* * *

As the initiator of this project, Abubaker Bagader began collecting and translating stories in 1993 for a sequel to *Assassination of Light: Modern Saudi Short Stories*, which he translated and Ava Heinrichsdorff edited. When Deborah Akers and Ava joined his effort to produce the second volume, he gave them the initial translations (and the Arabic originals) of a great many stories that had possibilities. As he collected these stories, he consulted with Saudi writers and literary specialists and found that the themes covered by the female writers pointed to an emerging movement in Saudi fiction writing. Since Westerners interested in Arab culture usually ask first about the status and lifestyle of women, it was clear that a collection of stories written by women would be of interest in the English-speaking world.

As a researcher and professor in the social sciences, Bagader was drawn to those stories with particular sociocultural content and that seemed to comment poignantly on what it means to be human. These stories seemed valid not only as representative Saudi fiction, but also as social commentary.

* * *

While Deborah Akers was living in Jeddah and doing fieldwork for a Ph.D. in anthropology, she and Abubaker discovered a mutual enthusiasm for making Saudi Arabian fiction more available to Western readers. Believing strongly in the necessity of people speaking for themselves, they concluded that this could be best achieved through a translation project. Deborah thus became the preliminary editor and second translator, who cross-referenced Abubaker's close-to-the-text translations against the Arabic originals. After many collective discussions, the three coeditors agreed on the stories to be included.

In Saudi Arabia, Deborah conducted her daily affairs as a Saudi woman would—dressing, speaking, and interacting with the women in their domain. She discovered that the similarities between Arab and North American women were surprisingly greater than their differences, with both juggling professional and family lives. She witnessed the literary success of rather young Saudi women—most in their twenties and thirties—who are not only managing motherhood and families but also their education and literary careers. Their tenacity and creative responses to challenge were inspirational. It is this insight into the lives of Saudi women that Deborah brought to this volume.

* * *

Ava M. Heinrichsdorff served as the final editor, polishing the stories to meet Western literary expectations while being careful to clarify and not to distort the author's intentions. Born in Hungary, she came from a cross-cultural background and a mobile family and eventually settled in the United States. Her son emigrated from the United States to Saudi Arabia, and it was through him that she met Abubaker and became involved in editing *Assassination of Light* and *Voices of Change*. Her graduate studies and professional work have always been multicultural: in international literatures and folk dance, in teaching foreign students, and in her own writings.

As a fiction writer, Ava is interested in the value of the stories in this volume both as entertainment and as educational devices that introduce different ways of evaluating situations and confronting problems. Her travels have taught her that it is all too easy to assume that our cultural habits are "human nature," when in fact "human nature" is amazingly diverse.

* * *

We are grateful to a number of people who helped make this project possible. First, we would like to thank the contributors for permission to include their work and Dr. Abdul-Aziz Al-Sebail, who graciously translated some of the stories, wrote the biographies of the contributors, and created the glossary. We are also indebted to Dr. Müge Galin for her cultural commentary and proofreading throughout the various stages of the project. Many thanks go to Don Mark for cheerfully and efficiently typing the original manuscript.

We have written the transliterations of the Arabic names according to the authors' preferences, but have also included in "About the Authors" at the back of the book a version of the authors' names transliterated according to the rules of the Library of Congress. We are especially grateful to Dr. Dona Straley for her assistance in this regard.

This project would not have been completed without the help of these individuals, as well as countless others who helped us generously along the way.

A. Bagader
A. M. Heinrichsdorff
D. S. Akers

Introduction

*Abubaker Bagader,
Ava M. Heinrichsdorff & Deborah S. Akers*

In Saudi Arabia, contemporary literature serves as an increasingly powerful medium through which women's voices can be heard. The stories in this collection dramatize some of the current interests and concerns of contemporary Arab women. They also present Arab women's approaches to the art of fiction—approaches that sometimes differ significantly from the expectations of Westerners. These writers discuss tacitly the kinds of issues that Western women can debate loudly.

Western readers will identify with some of these women's concerns and will be surprised by others. Many of these are protest stories, and one of the challenges to the reader is to decide what is being protested against and what is being accepted as custom. For instance, in "The Last Dream," Muna ad-Dhukayr is clearly protesting the tribalism that considers every outsider, even a neighbor, a permanent foreigner—one aspect of the clannishness of a culture in which endogamous marriage is customary. But is she protesting or accepting as normal the way the family pulls a girl out of school—forever—simply because she is pretty and therefore vulnerable?

Since family life dominates most Arab women's existence, women's issues revolve primarily around the family and the neighborhood. The best and worst things that can happen take place within the family unit, as these stories bear out. Yet might any of these domestic subjects represent larger political or social issues that are too dangerous to confront directly? Perhaps they do; seeing possible connections is another challenge for Western readers.

Some Arab family customs are significantly different from those of Europe and North America. One example is the role of fathers, who are often presented here as distant, punishing, and terrifying—from a Western perspective, even abusive. Husbands sometimes take on this paternal role toward their wives, who are often much younger than they are; their wives might therefore remain in a juvenile role as they mature and age. (And brothers often seem to be practicing those future male roles at their sisters' expense, with the tacit approval of their parents.) Some of these stories clearly protest against that style of fatherhood.

Another difference between Western expectations and Saudi reality lies in the concept of romantic love. Although many female characters in these stories hope for such love, with fantasies based on song lyrics or popular literature rather than experience, few really expect it, and fewer still value it more than economic security. As we see in "If Only It Were Pity," when the marriage contract isn't an advantageous one, being "in love" gives a woman no social status and contributes nothing to her own feeling of self-worth. Since a man and woman are not allowed to get to know each other before marriage, the love that some of the characters experience is often a superficial though intense "love at first sight." The deeper kind of love that *can* develop from learning to know each other truly well can develop, but only after marriage. (Of course, even in Western cultures, getting to know each other before marriage is a relatively recent development.) Sex isn't assumed to be an expression of love between partners, but an obligation that one might enjoy, like homemaking and parenthood

Western readers might assume that it is human nature to require some solitude, some private space, and some personal property that others won't invade. But these stories demonstrate no need for solitary time or inviolable personal space or property; such desires can even be considered deviant in the Saudi context.

Westerners might also think that a detailed appreciation of the natural world is part of human nature and should have a place in any literature. Yet the natural world is rarely mentioned in these stories. This is because nature—in the case of Saudi Arabia, the outdoors with its heat—is something to escape from. Unlike the desert-loving Bedouin, some of Saudi Arabia's literati seem so urban that they scarcely notice nature.

Drunkenness and adultery are sins according to the

Qur'an. Yet both crimes do occur in Saudi Arabia, and in the stories dealing with these problems, the victimized wives do not react in the ways Western readers might expect. Of course, both Arab and Western women resent mistreatment, but Arab legal and social systems make divorce more problematic for Arab women, which may well involve losing custody of their children. The authors of these stories are clearly encouraging women to free themselves from their tormentors, yet the heroines *never* visualize the offending husbands being publicly punished in a traditional way. Not one of these wives even imagines bringing legal charges against her husband. One reason is that in traditional cultures people rarely think of justice as something that comes from a formal institution such as a court. Protection comes only from one's family or clan, who are expected to support and defend their members. (Of course, this leaves women who don't have strong and sympathetic families quite defenseless.) In this collection the family and social cohesion are celebrated, or their absence is mourned. Family solidarity is prized more than conspicuous individuality.

In terms of style, some of these stories read like parables. Unlike Western fiction, in which the characters' individuality is of crucial importance and is presented through specific details of behavior, interests, competencies, imagination, or environment, some of the characters in these stories seem more like symbols of human problems than fully realized individuals.

Islamic art must avoid the realistic representation of "anything that casts a shadow"—especially people—so artists express reality abstractly, geometrically, or otherwise symbolically. Some of the stories in this collection remind us of such art works, and of the marvelous shadow puppet theater of Turkey, Java, or other Islamic cultures. These stories tend to summarize more than dramatize, even in climactic scenes. They provide few details of character or setting. Here the characters often resemble Everyman and Everywoman rather than specific individuals. Writers may also prefer the parable approach for fear that specific details would come too close to providing easily recognizable truths about families or friends.

Some will ask, why these particular stories? Do they represent typical life in Saudi Arabia? Hardly, any more than a collection of Western fiction dealing with child abuse, prejudice, or addiction would automatically represent the norm.

Although the situations portrayed in these stories are not typical, they are, nonetheless, very real. This collection confronts many cultural and literary presuppositions that Western readers might hold. The editors hope that these stories prove intriguing and thought-provoking to their new audience as well as deepening their understanding of the Saudi world.

The Origin of the Stories

The stories in this collection come from three sources. Most were first published in local Saudi newspapers, such as *Okaz, al-Bilad,* and *al-Madinah;* others were published in magazines such as *Sayyidati* and *Hawwa.* And still others appeared as part of collections by publishing houses in Lebanon or Egypt, since these are a recent innovation in the kingdom. All were first written and published in Arabic; they have been translated into English by the editors and Abdulaziz Alsebail for the purposes of this North American edition.

Until the 1960s and 1970s, only a handful of Saudi women were writing and publishing, for men dominated the printed word. The few women who did write, such as Samirah Khashuqji and Najjat Khayyat, were from privileged families who could afford to have their daughters educated abroad. These women had a definite social agenda for writing. By the 1970s Saudi women who chose to write were no longer limited to the upper classes. This is due to the movement toward educating girls that took place in the 1960s, when King Faysal's wife was responsible for opening the first public schools for young Saudi girls. Later, the oil boom of the 1970s stimulated the founding of more publishing houses in the kingdom, which made publishing more accessible. By the 1980s and 1990s, there was a literary renaissance in Saudi Arabia and a true emergence of Saudi women writers, to such an extent that a casual observer of any newspaper or magazine would comment on the predominance of women's names. Women also were allowed to become members of several literary clubs, where their work was evaluated and critiqued by their peers.

This collection is divided into four parts: Life Passages; Social Issues; Love: Romantic, Requited, and Otherwise; and Memories. From these stories three general themes emerge:

presenting the self anew, self-assertion within the household, and the self facing others in the larger social context. The evolving concepts of the self, identity, and women's roles emphasized in these stories, are set in a specific sociocultural framework.

In Part 1, the writers ponder emerging womanhood and explore the process by which adolescent girls shape their self-identity. Writers present such questions as "Who is the Saudi female?," "Who should she be?," and "How should she be treated?" Najat Khayyat in "Had I Been Male" portrays a girl who objects to being sold as a commodity. In Badriyyah al-Bishir's "School Diaries," there are three forces from which the young girl wants to be free: polygyny, male dominance, and the oppression of other women. In "Tears of Joy and Sorrow," Jamilah Fatani emphasizes that education is a liberating force that must not be denied to females. In "Why Shouldn't I Be Like Her?", Fatani asserts that fathers should rethink their priorities. When they neglect their responsibility for their children, stepmothers can be cruel and punitive. The story idealizes sisterhood as a liberating force, implying a sense of feminism in the making. Here we encounter stories in which women must cope with compromising circumstances in the family context. Some of these women prove equal to the challenge, while others fail.

The following stories represent capable women who are able to cope and at the same time play new roles as active, productive women in their society. We see roles shifting in Sharifah ash-Shamlan's "Complete Calm." The male personality is no longer the guardian and custodian; the mature woman is capable of playing that role with confidence and responsibility. In "The Duties of a Working Wife," Wafa Munawwar highlights a professional woman who is also a good mother, wife, and hostess. In "To Celebrate Being a Woman," Fatimah al-ᶜUtaybi gives us the strong voice of a woman who thinks that if men cannot face contemporary challenges, then women must either do so themselves or raise sons who can do so.

Patriarchy is more overtly condemned in the stories about women who are less able to cope. In Sharifah ash-Shamlan's "Zainab," if women do not reflect the desired image for a Saudi woman, they may be stigmatized as sinners. Fatimah al-ᶜUtaybi's "Just Give Me the Right to Dream" shows how women who are merely used to fulfill the male partner's dreams become marginalized and lose their self-esteem. Dreams seem to be the only means for the heroine to think of herself as an equal partner. In "The Dove Is a Woman," Nurah al-Ghamdi emphasizes that when a woman does not fight for her liberty, she might lose her very sanity. One solution is to speak out; then perhaps someone will listen.

The stories in Part 2 illustrate how women's lives are shaped in reaction to larger social issues such as poverty, alcoholism, drug abuse, infidelity, and infertility. Fatima ad-Dawsari's "Saffron" explores issues of poverty and the need to alleviate suffering, while Khayriyyah as-Saqqaf's "The Loss" illustrates the devastation of an impoverished woman. "Saffron" shows a middle-class woman doing a good deed by helping a poor man. "The Loss" illustrates how sometimes a woman loses touch with reality and is unable to break ties with her protectors. Such a woman may turn to a worse tyrant than the one she is trying to escape. If she remains quiet, she loses. In "A Puzzling Whirlwind," Amal cAbdul-Hamid asserts that if fertility is a woman's only value, then she will always be on the defensive. The story strongly advocates that women develop a career, as the mother advised. Even the mother-in-law realizes how the protagonist's professional status helps compensate for her husband's neglect and earns her respect in the community. In "Wednesday Night," Badriyyah al-Bishir shows that if her marriage is a disaster, like Hai's marriage to an alcoholic, a wife's total dependence upon a man can make her unproductive and self-destructive. As-Saqqaf evaluates the choice between being dominated and being oneself in "The Reflection."

Saudi women writers also like to write about love and romance. In Part 3 we see the consequences of women's changing expectations with regard to love. Qumashah al- cUlayyan's "I Will Not Return" highlights the evolution from accepting an arranged marriage as fate to rejecting a marriage in which a woman is not loved. The protagonist remarries when she finds a man who sincerely loves her. The theme of changing expectations is articulated again in "If Only It Were Pity." Here, Lamia Baeshen dramatizes the way that true love makes one risk tragedy. Samirah Khashuqji shows in "Fall Nights" that love and communication are dialogical: it is only when the two partners talk with each other and work toward mutual understanding that a healthy and joyous married life can be realized. The story shows how a woman's conscious choice to be in an equal relationship can prevent confusion and boredom. In "A Single-Winged Bird," Lamia Baeshen illustrates how difficult a double identity is to endure in a homogeneous society. Even in love, the protagonist suffers because she looks different.

In this traditional society, young girls in love might respond to the cultural limitations imposed upon them with strategies that range from white lies to dreaming to death. We find in Muna ad-Dhukayr's "The Last Dream," for example, that when a woman cannot fulfill her romantic desires, she can defy tradition by allowing herself to dream what she wants—her love, and her death—despite the cultural sanctions against trespassing ethnic and cultural boundaries. In "I Never Lied," Qumashah al-ᶜUlayyan demonstrates that full honesty between marriage partners requires respect, love, and security from sanctions. Even though the protagonist wants to be sincerely honest, it is vital for her to lie to her husband about an earlier flirtation. "The Game" by Sarah Buhaymid shows that women must be fully aware of the men they are flirting with and the conditions of their game. Otherwise, they can be hurt. Women are portrayed as cherishers of true love and good memories in Najat Khayyat's "Take Me With You." A good woman is one who is capable of sharing love and understanding with her husband without necessarily forgetting a loving ex-partner.

Saudi Arabian women do not only write about themselves. Part 4 shows that tradition affects all members of society. It can be a limiting force, but it can also expand an individual's experience. "The Madman" by Jamilah Fatani shows that it takes a wise girl to appreciate the wisdom, vision, and humanity in the *ustadh*, something the rest of the community fails to see. "Burqan's Ghost" by Nurah al-Ghamdi belongs to the mysteries and mythologies of rural communities, but enforces the strong voice of justice, and the community's belief that the village will flourish only when justice prevails.

No collection of Arabic stories can escape the spell of Shahrazad and her Arabian Nights. The new Saudi Arabian Shahrazad might have an agenda different from that of entertaining Shahriar. As Raja' ᶜAlim shows in "One Thousand Braids and a Governess," her consciousness seems to contain conflicting memories, dreams, and worries. Only through the reflection and integration of these different aspects of her identity can she sail into modern womanhood.

These short stories dramatize several points. First, that Arab women are changing both in their roles and in the ways they think about themselves. The stories focus on the identity and the representation of females, and on the serious search for new and fresh perspectives. Second, the stories highlight means of negotiation and conflict resolution different from those prevalent in the West; in this regard perhaps Arab women are closer to some of their sisters in African and Asian cultures. Saudi women tend to be cautious and nonconfrontational, and rely on time to decide the outcome of a conflict. These stories voice discontent and rebellion by focusing on abuses and the neglect that some Saudi women endure. Saudi women writers dramatize abusive situations in order to make them focal points for dialogue, questioning, and reflection by both men and women.

Saudi Society: The Context for the Stories

The people of Arabia inhabit a peninsula that stretches from southern Syria to the Indian Ocean and from the Red Sea to the Persian/Arab Gulf. The Kingdom of Saudi Arabia occupies about nine-tenths of the Arabian peninsula, which is shared to the east with the United Arab Emirates, Oman, Qatar, and Kuwait, and to the south with Yemen. The capital city of Riyadh, and the towns of Jeddah, Mekka, and Dammam/Dhahran constitute the largest urban areas.

Although the kingdom is divided geophysically into six major regions, and each region has its own particular history and ecological variability, the people of Arabia are culturally and socially homogenous. Nejd, geographically the inner region, is the political center. Surrounded by desert, it is a rocky plateau with pockets of fertile oases. To the south of Nejd is the Rub al-Khali, or "Empty Quarter," one of the largest deserts in the world, traditionally inhabited by camel pastoralists. To the north of Nejd is the Northern region, characterized by plateaus, ancient lava flows, and *wadis*, or river beds. To the west, extending to the Red Sea, is the Hejaz, which supports the holy city of Mekka, as well as a number of oasis cities along the ancient caravan route between Syria and Yemen. The rugged mountainous region of Asir, strikingly different from any other in the country, lies directly to the south of the Hejaz. The oil-rich eastern province of al-Hasa is the sixth region of the kingdom. Located on the Arabian Gulf, it is characterized by spring-fed oasis settlements and bustling coastal cities.

Occupied since ancient times, the Arabian peninsula has been the home of urban-based civilizations as well as of pastoral nomads. In pre-Islamic times there was no single polity governing the peninsula, but small independent kingdoms instead: the Dilmunites to the east, the Nabateans to the north, and the South Arabians to the southwest. Arabia is also the birthplace of Islam. In the first decades of the seventh century the Prophet Muhammad brought together the people of Mekka, Medina, and surrounding areas under the banner of Islam. From here the new religion spread throughout the peninsula and beyond. Centuries later the holy cities, which were ruled by local *sharifs*, came under the rule of the Ottoman Turks. In the 1700s, an alliance was made between the ruling house of Saud and the religious leader Muhammad Wahhab. This union officially established Wahhabism, a fundamentalist movement, in the heart of Arabia, where it prevails even today. At the turn of this century, Ibn Saud took control of the major provinces of Arabia through a military campaign and forged the present kingdom of Saudi Arabia.

Islam pervades all aspects of Saudi culture and demands that its followers accept religion as a total way of life. Not only must the believer accept the theological premises of Islamic monotheism, but he or she must also pray five times daily; pay *zakat*, or charity; fast during Ramadan; and if possible, make the pilgrimage to Mekka at least once in one's lifetime. Wahhabi theology reinforces these precepts by stressing doctrinal purity. They oppose, for example, saint worship, any kind of prophetic cults, or any intermediary between God and his human worshippers, and they tend to be strict scripturalists, closely following the Hanbali school of law.

The traditional primary kinship unit in Saudi society is the *ahl*, or extended family, in which a senior male, his wife or wives, unmarried children, and married sons with their wives and children all live together. Polygyny is allowed according to Islamic tradition, although it is rarely practiced in the kingdom today. A man may have up to four wives at the same time, but only on condition that he is able to treat them equally and provide each a separate place of residence. Polygyny is most commonly found among the wealthy or the elite. But it is in decline in modern Saudi Arabia, as more young women are refusing to become the second wife.

Despite the fact that the Saudi family unit is definitely patriarchal, the role of women is quite central and their influence cannot be overlooked. On the one hand, the mother and daughter are in a submissive position to the patriarch and his sons within the family; on the other hand the females wield power in the home, which is their sphere of authority. Since women marry rather early, they are quite experienced and in command by the time they are in their early thirties. Consequently, the senior female is usually still of reproductive age when her older daughters or her first daughters-in-law begin to bear children. A woman moves into her husband's household upon marriage; in the case of divorce, she moves with her young children back to the house of her own parents.

In the ideal model of a Saudi extended family, the son continues to live with his father after he marries, with his wife joining him. As a daughter matures and marries, she moves out to her husband's residence. The sons are expected to remain in the household until the death of their father, at which time they are free to leave and start their own households. However, in practice, not all the sons stay close: some may migrate to other locations for work, starting their own households there. Also, in modern urban circumstances, there is a trend for married couples to move into their own homes. However, it is rare for the parents to be left without any sons living nearby.

Marriage is the primary goal in a young girl's life, and her parents begin to make marriage arrangements for her as soon as she reaches adolescence. In an urban setting girls marry between seventeen and twenty years of age. Villagers tend to marry from three to six years earlier, with some girls marrying as young as fourteen, the boys at seventeen. This early age reflects both the fact that girls' education is considered less important and the need to harness their sexuality before they bring disgrace to their parents.

Since marriage is regarded as an alliance for the whole family, it is a serious matter to be negotiated by parents and not by the young people themselves. Normally the boy's family initiates the search for a bride, kinship relations being the most important factor. The preferred marriage is between patrilateral parallel cousins—between a girl and her father's brother's son, for example. Such a marriage is perceived as being particularly advantageous, because it permits property to remain within the family and unites young people of relatively similar backgrounds. Moreover, both sides are already well acquainted with the bride and groom, who may have been living together in one household all their lives. It also allows for an easier transition for the bride, since her new in-laws are family members with whom she has had a close relationship since childhood.

Female members and friends of the boy's family identify eligible girls of suitable families when it is time for the boy to marry. They make the initial inquiries to determine whether the girl is free to marry or has been promised to another. Through the process of elimination, the kinswomen choose a girl who appears best suited to the match.

The first time the girl is involved in the search is when *khitbah*, the first offer of marriage, is made by the prospective groom's family through an intermediary. Yet she is almost never directly involved in the negotiations; nor is the boy. Customs vary as to who makes the offer and whether or not the girl is consulted in the matter. In social geographer Motoko Katakura's (1977:83) description of Hejazi village life, it may be either the mother or the father of the boy who approaches the girl's parents. The normal response by the girl's father is to ask the family of the potential groom to wait for an answer. During this period, members of the girl's family consult one another, and the mother indirectly asks her daughter for her opinion of the suitor. Although it would appear unseemly for the girl to be directly involved in the negotiations, she holds veto power; if she does not consent to the match, the marriage will not take place. Today, some urban families arrange a series of formal gatherings during which the boy and girl meet to become acquainted.

If the girl consents to the marriage, negotiations begin concerning the *mahr*, or bridewealth. According to Islamic law, the bridewealth may be paid in two installments. The *muqaddam*, or advanced portion, is paid by the groom's family at the time of the engagement. The *muakhkhar*, or deferred portion, is given when the marriage is terminated or the husband dies; it is intended to provide the wife with a measure of economic security should she lose her husband. The husband pays this to the wife in the case of divorce, and the estate or next of kin pays the sum to the widow at the time of her husband's death (Katakura 1977:85).

The money provided by the bridewealth is most often used by the bride's family to furnish her with items needed for her marriage. According to Saudi anthropologist Soraya Altorki (1986:138–39), it was customary among the elite in Jeddah for the father of the bride to furnish several rooms for her in her father-in-law's house. In the 1970s the amount of the mahr was increased to include enough furnishings for a small apartment. Presently, at least among the elite, the mahr is set at around 100,000 *riyals* (or US$29,400). The groom's family places the money directly in a bank account for the bride. The Dutch scholar Hurgronje (1931:126) reported that 100 years ago poor urban dwellers asked as high a price as they could for the mahr, because the possessions a woman brought to the marriage were all that she would own should the marriage fail. In the case of a man from a lower income bracket, the mahr is substantially less; it may be omitted altogether in a case of cousin marriage where the families are close.

Traditionally, close family members of the bride provided gifts for her hope chest such as new dresses, gold jewelry, and perfumes. In modern urban settings the bride's family gives her expensive gifts of gold and jewelry. These gifts, which can be exchanged for their value in riyals, form the bride's personal savings account. In case of divorce, the woman may take these items with her when she returns to her father's house. Both the mahr and the other gifts are traditionally arranged in order to assure a woman's financial security.

After the bridewealth is agreed upon, a date is set for drawing up and signing the marriage contract. The fathers of the bride and groom, accompanied by male witnesses, meet with the local religious leader for the signing of the contract, which bears the names of the couple to be married and the amount agreed upon for the bridewealth. The bride and groom each receive a copy of the document (Katakura 1977:85).

Once married, the Arabian woman's first challenge is to prove her fertility, as her husband's goal is to establish his own nuclear family. Therefore the young couple tries to have a child within the first year of their marriage. It is within the context of the family that children learn appropriate roles and are taught the fundamental values within Saudi society. It is interesting to note in this context that the writers included here focus on the bond between husband (or lover) and wife and have relatively little to say about a woman's role as mother.

Marriage is a more difficult adjustment for the woman, because she has to move into her husband's household, where she is expected to adjust not only to her husband, but to all his family members. Therefore, Saudis rarely attribute divorce to the incompatibility of husband and wife, blaming instead conflicts between mother-in-law and daughter-in-law, or between the wife's family and the husband's family. Marriage is perceived not as a sacramental union but as a civil one, legalized by a document—signed by two parties—that can be broken. Therefore divorce is not uncommon, nor does it carry much stigma among most groups.

One area where women feel relatively powerless is in the issue of divorce: only men have the formal right to divorce their wives. They do this by stating three times before witnesses "I divorce you; I divorce you; I divorce you." But while this ritual of divorce may be a simple utterance, the actual dissolution of a marriage can be a long drawn-out affair, involving extensive interfamily negotiations. Although a woman cannot initiate divorce, she can bring one about by returning to her parent's house and then having her parents request the divorce.

The usual pattern is for husband and wife to separate several times before a divorce is finalized. The first time the husband tells his wife he divorces her, she must return to her family's household. After some time has passed a reconciliation may be arranged by the family members on both sides. The husband may then send expensive gifts to his wife; if she wishes to return to him, she will accept the gifts. Years later a second divorce and yet another reconciliation may occur. A third divorce, however, terminates the marriage, and the woman is then free to remarry. While it is possible for all three divorces to occur at the same time, the majority take place over long periods of time, involving a number of reconciliations.

In the past, husbands from wealthy families in Jeddah used conditional divorce to control their wives' behavior (Altorki

1986:81). It was not uncommon for a husband to divorce his wife once or twice to keep her in line, rather than out of real desire to dissolve the marriage bond. This resulted in a potentially precarious husband-wife relationship and was a source of considerable insecurity for the women.

If family members or a counselor cannot succeed in reconciling the couple, then the divorce is finalized. If the husband has initiated the divorce, the woman keeps the bridewealth as well as any personal possessions—such as gold, jewelry, and clothes—she acquired during the marriage. The newly divorced woman is not allowed to leave her house for four months and ten days. This waiting period, or *'idda,* is observed to determine whether a woman is pregnant from the marriage and, if so, to bestow legitimacy upon the offspring.

In case of divorce, Islamic law allows children to remain in the mother's custody until the boys are seven to nine years old and the girls reach puberty. The mother oversees her children's upbringing in her father's house. In the event that she remarries, then the children move back to their father's house where they are supervised by their paternal grandmother or their stepmother.

The death of the senior male results in the breakup of the extended family. According to Altorki (1986:82–84), what happens when a senior male dies depends upon the age of his sons. If the household head leaves young children behind, then a close male agnate such as his brother assumes responsibility for them and the widow. If the sons are mature, then they assume responsibility for the household, including dependent family members: the mother and unmarried sisters and brothers. Often the eldest son, if he is financially able, either merges his father's household with his own or maintains the two separate households.

Women without husbands find it difficult to live alone in Saudi society. This forces female dependents to select a male relative with whom to live. Mothers usually choose a son to stay with, based upon their compatibility with the son and his wife and his ability to support her. It is not unusual for unmarried daughters to live with the mother, if the son agrees to provide for them as well. If a widow has no familial support, she can apply to live in a *rubat,* or charity hostel; these are found in large urban centers.

The profile of the Saudi Arabian woman is changing considerably as more women pursue a higher education and join the work force. An educated wife is considered more desirable, as young working men show a preference for brides who can contribute to the household income. Young women, on the other hand, are not only asking for the right to work in their marriage contracts but also for households separate from their husbands' families. Both of these changes will strengthen the position of Saudi women, giving them higher status in their households and more control over their lives.

References

Altorki, Soraya
1986 *Women in Arabia: Ideology and Behavior Among the Elite.* New York: Columbia University Press.
Hurgronje, Christiaan Snouck
1931 *Mekka in the Latter Part of the 19th Century.* Leiden: E. J. Brill.
Katakura, Motoko
1977 *Bedouin Village: A Study of a Saudi Arabian People in Transition.* Tokyo: University of Tokyo Press.

PART ONE
Life Passages

Had I Been Male

Najat Khayyat

This story cries out against the fate of women in a traditional society in which marriage is supposed to be a woman's ultimate shelter and protection. Sometimes it can be a miserable exchange. Here a young orphan girl (for a fatherless child is considered an orphan in Arabia), for whom marriage should be a salvation, is imprisoned in the traditional "shelter," by her "protectors."

—Editors

You will wonder when you hear that my price was only three thousand *riyals*. It was paid in cash to my maternal uncle. One night a group of men met at my uncle's house and recited the *al-Fatihah*[1] to end my freedom and my youth. This kind of meeting should have been held in our own home and my father should have been the one to receive my price, but fate had decided to relieve him of this heavy burden,[2] letting him die and disappear from Mother's and my life.

In her poverty my poor mother had to eulogize the fact that I am female. Had I been male, my father's house still would have been open, and I would have relieved her of depending on the crumbs from my uncle's table.[3] Had I been male, I would have become a wall to protect my mother from the difficult times.[4]

That night's meeting was the first time that fury blossomed inside me merely because I am female. Now the hatred of my degrading femininity has sunk deep inside me. It is socially unacceptable for me as a female to work to save myself from the humiliation of needing the help of others. It is socially unacceptable for me to stand in the sun and enjoy its warmth, because a fly might sting me; instead, I must stay in the decaying darkness where I am eaten away by the rottenness. They call this safety.

No, I did not revolt. I stayed miserable and suffocated. Am I not a female?

When that ugly old woman, a stranger to us, came to our door and asked my mother to sew an *abayah,* Mother sighed with relief. She welcomed her warmly and escorted her into the house, despite the fact that she doesn't even know how to use scissors. But my mother sensed who she was and what she wanted from a house where there is a young and pretty girl who could become a future bride for her son. All of this took shape quickly in my mother's head as she was welcoming the woman and sitting beside her with all the etiquette of hospitality. From behind the door I watched them curiously.

Then I saw my mother rushing toward me. "Comb your long hair, put on a cheerful dress, and bring our guest a cup of coffee!" I quickly did what my mother ordered me to do, and shyly entered the room carrying a tray with a cup of coffee for the guest.

The woman looked at me appraisingly and smiled. I modestly lowered my head. Her eyes became like a wicked cat's, examining me as if there might be something artificial about my body. Perhaps I'd put on some part like wooden or plastic fingernails, or pearl teeth?

After she was sure that the merchandise was God-created and there was nothing artificial about my beauty, whispers between my mother and the ugly old woman closed the deal.

It was socially shameful for me to overhear such an important conversation as the one in which my life was sold to a man.

What man? If he'd been her son, the woman's arranging might have been reasonable, or at least logical. But he was her brother, only two years younger than she, who had spent most of his life living like a Don Juan and now wanted to retire with a delicious meal that might return him to the good life.

Nervously rubbing her hands together, my mother rushed to discuss this urgent matter with my uncle. "Oh my brother, he is perfect. He owns a house and several shops. His income is quite reasonable. He owns a fabric store. He is an old man, mature and balanced, able to watch over her, since she is so young. He will take care of her and let her wear the silk she has dreamed of."

My uncle seemed relieved to hear what she had to say and answered, "All right, Sister, since you liked him, I don't have any objection to the marriage." Then, pretending to think, he added, "Let's wait awhile and ask about him in the neighborhood. Let's see who knows him."

My mother responded quickly. "There is no need, my brother; his sister told me everything about his life and character, and his income will enable my daughter to live a comfortable, even luxurious, life." My mother chose to believe her. "Isn't that what I have wanted for her all along?"

The conversation finished quickly, more quickly than selling a small chicken to a man who will eat it during the '*id*.[5]

On the wedding day I was not moved by happiness, nor was my heart gay as a bride's should be. I was miserable, and furious about being female. Had I been male, I would not have been buried in this coffin they call a bride's gown, or celebrated in a funeral crowded with curious neighborhood women who were envying me for this rich groom. My spring of fifteen years would not have been buried in a cold autumn bedroom that aged me abruptly.

I soon discovered many things that the ugly old woman did not tell my mother. I discovered that there is a whip that destroys the meaning of being human whenever that meaning starts to take shape inside me. I discovered things my mother did not tell me, either: that my innocent breaths would mix with his rotten pantings, and that the stale crumbs from my uncle's table were a thousand times sweeter than the whole loaves that I must pay for every night by lying with a dead body with fossilized eyes, enveloped in the smell of the grave . . . pay for with my life.

One day when I could no longer endure it, I rushed to visit my mother to cry on her breast over the degradation of my femininity. "Rescue me from this man!" I begged her with the innocence of a girl and the suffering of a woman.

My mother moved her hand over my hair as if she were adding to my bindings. "Be patient," she said. "Otherwise you're not from a good family. There is no other protection for us, Daughter—your house is your only shelter and protection."[6]

I cried and shouted out from inside, "Shelter? Protection? Did it liberate me from this prison to be sold to the first passerby? You are oppressing me, my mother."

She looked at me firmly and her look said, "You're a female. It is not my mistake, not my oppression. Nothing can be done."

Notes

1. Al-Fatihah is the opening chapter of the *Quran;* it is usually read during the formal proposal for marriage.
2. A sarcastic remark on the custom of bride-price.
3. Upon the death of the father, the "house" breaks up. The mother, daughters, and young sons must reside with the closest living male relative, usually the father's brother. When a mother dies, however, there is no change in the residence except that the father may bring in a new wife.
4. If the son is of age and financially able to support his widowed mother, then she will stay with her son.
5. Marriage negotiations can be long, protracted affairs. The fact that discussions were finished in the length of time it takes to sell a chicken to a hungry man, perhaps five minutes, indicates that the girl's welfare was not carefully considered.
6. Most women are not in a position to be economically productive and must rely upon either their husbands or male relatives to support them.

School Diaries

Badriyyah al-Bishir

This story blames women's suffering on polygyny, men's absolute authority, and women's misunderstanding and distrust of each other. These schoolgirls apparently have done nothing to deserve their mistreatment. The protagonist asks, "Why must women be victimized by other women who assume the dominant male role, especially in an all-female environment such as a girl's school?"
—*Editors*

One day my father shouted at my mother, "Next Thursday I will marry another woman and bring her here."

My mother cried, begging him to do anything else he pleased, but not to bring a new bride into her house.

I was very young when my father left us. We stopped seeing him so often. In the beginning he used to come every other day. Then later we didn't see him except when he brought supplies for the house. But as my brother, Saeed, grew, it was he who brought home provisions and my father disappeared altogether.

* * *

Saeed inspected my room every day. He searched my things and censored my phone calls. He searched for something only he knew. Even though he was only two years older than me, he began to assume his male right to shout at me.

Once he ripped up photographs of me taken with some girlfriends and said, "You look like immodest girls, wearing these tight dresses with slits on the side." I cried then. He kept the picture of one of my girlfriends in his drawer. Even my books were not safe from his scrutiny. But I learned how to hide books inside my dresses hanging in the closet—I tied them at the waist so nothing could fall out. I also hid my expensive perfumes among them.

One morning when I was combing my hair, I tied it back and pinned it with a red and white metal clip. When I finished I reached for lipstick from over the mirror. I drew a light line and a dot on each cheek for blush. I stopped quickly when Saeed violently pushed open the bedroom door. He saw me and said reproachfully, "Do you really plan to go to school looking like that?"

Before he could become angry, I rushed to the bathroom and washed my face.

* * *

There were thirty of us in the classroom. My friends Hind and Turfa and I were seated at the back. We hid our special things in our desks and inside our black *abayahs*,[1] which we put on carefully as we left. Hind brought videotapes. From time to time, Turfa brought foreign fashion magazines full of pictures of women in beautiful dresses colored like our dreams when we whispered to the face of the moon, which was almost never full.

We planted our faces in our shared reading book. Each of us sometimes claimed to have forgotten her book at home, so as to be able to share and talk with the others. As our fingers followed the last words we heard one of the girls reading in the front row, Hind asked me, "Where are the photos?"

"Saeed tore them up."

Turfa interrupted us: "Last night Abdullah entered my room as I was talking on the phone. He stood close to me. He circled around me twice. Then suddenly, he grabbed the phone away from me, but when all he heard was a busy signal, he shouted, 'Who were you talking to?' "

We all were very scared, and asked her, "Did he find out?"

Before she could answer, the teacher's shrill voice came through, "What is this noise in the back? I will separate you if you don't keep quiet."

Which of the two voices scared us more? Our hearts were

beating hard as our dreams were torn apart in the empty space as light as snow. We wondered fearfully, "Did he find out that she was talking to a boy?"

Bodies stretched in front of us. The class stood up. What was going on in the front? We heard the teacher at the head of the room ordering all of us: "Stand up!"

The first monitor struck her wooden ruler on the first desk and said, "Inspection!"

Ya Allah! Inspection! These school monitors and their frequent surprises never stopped. What kind of a day is it that begins with Saeed and finishes with school monitors? They were inspecting all the papers in our book bags. What did I have today? *The Arabian Nights* was inside my book bag. I'd borrowed it minutes ago from Norah. Fire inflamed my fear.

"Take out your book bag."

Only the good students in the front row sat down. We called them *dawafeer*, bookworms.

Merfet took out her case.

"And your *abayah* too!"

One school monitor threw out her books and notebooks on the desk. She turned the pages of Merfet's book. A small photo fell out. It was of Merfet and her father in her homeland by the sea. Now she only knew the heat of the summer and a cheap *abayah*, which she pulled over her small body when she left school. When the monitor tore up the photo, Merfet cried out, "We will never return home again, so why didn't you leave me my photo?"

As the monitor started to inspect the next row, my heart began to beat faster. Shahrazad of *Arabian Nights* would take me to the abyss.[2] She saves her own neck each time she tells one of her strange stories to Shahriar, the king. But, ya Allah! Who would save my neck from the Shahriar at my home when I went back?

"A mirror, lovely, my beauty."[3]

The girls laughed. The school monitor quickly turned toward us in back. She looked at us like a wildcat. The teacher rapped her ruler twice on the desk, asking for quiet and order. The students swallowed the rest of their laughter. One of them dropped her head between her palms and began to shake violently.

My hands began to move between my bag and the desk. I'll

fail to take out the book, I thought. But if it falls out, disaster will take place.

"Mashallah! You have colored magazines. What is this audacity?" Mai was asked.

The monitor turned to the other and winked. She handed her the magazine and she set it aside.

"Bring your mother tomorrow!"

"My mother is not at home, only my stepmother. She will gloat and convince my father to take me out of school," Mai answered.

I knew Saeed would shout at my mother, as my father once did, "I will not stay at home. This daughter of yours will humiliate us. That school doesn't teach her anything but insolence!"

"Shut up!" The monitor shouted at Mai, who was crying. As she advanced toward the row in front of ours, my knees weakened, my throat dried up, and once again my hands started to move between my bag and the desk.

"Whose photos are those?"

"My sister's wedding."

"What does your sister's wedding have to do with school? What is this nonsense?"

She threw the album on the table. The other monitor took it. She was joined by the teacher and they started to examine the photos and smile.

My mother would rock her head in her hands and mourn her luck, saying, "What will people say about me? They will say this is the upbringing of a weak mother."[4]

"Stand up."

"Yes, monitor!"

"Take out your book bag, *abayah*, and . . ."

I opened my bag and unfolded my *abayah*. The monitor's hand stretched to take out the books. The books appeared and with them, Shahriar's sword. My blood rushed to my face. I looked upward once, and downward a long time.

Notes

1. A black outer garment worn by women and adolescent girls whenever they are in public.

2. Shahrazak is more commonly called "Sheherazade" in the West.

3. "Sitt al-husn wa al-jamaal," meaning "good and lovely mistress," is an expression commonly used in pampering young girls. Here it is used sarcastically.

4. In Saudi culture children brought up by the mother without the presence of a father are thought to be undisciplined and spoiled. Of course this is stereotyping but it underscores the authoritarian role of the father, who disciplines the children.

Tears of Joy and Sorrow

Jamilah Fatani

Since traditional male authority imprisons women in the name of protecting them, it is the women who have to fight for liberation. Education is probably the most liberating force for a woman. Has Ahlam repressed her fury at her father, or forgiven him? Or has her culture never allowed her any fury at all?

—Editors

The big university hall was filled with cheer.[1] The faces were smiling, the eyes eager, the rows crowded with women; the air conditioning provided a pleasant breeze. The girls, proudly wearing their uniforms, were spread across the stage in wonderful formation like birds or flowers of spring.

One of them overheard a whisper from a cheerful woman in a front row. "My daughter Ahlam is graduating! Her name will be announced, and she will walk in the procession with her classmates. Praise be to you, oh Allah, you did not disappoint me!"

"Congratulations!" another woman replied. "May Allah grant her every success. My niece is graduating, too. She is like my own daughter. I brought her up, along with her brothers, after their mother, my sister, passed away. May Allah show His mercy on her! This is my happiest moment, seeing her in this great affair."

Ahlam, waiting along with her classmates, scrutinized the faces surrounding her. Was that Sawsan! That calm and venerable lady? This was the first time she had looked so free. And was that Afaf, also looking free, and clearly enjoying herself?

Nearby Huda examined a paper and happily said, "See, it is my name. Praise be to Allah. It has never been written correctly before. I've always had to bear the addition of a letter or a dot to my family name—people are so generous. But today it doesn't matter whether they wrote my name right or wrong. It's enough that all know that I have passed! Ilhamdillah! Praise be to Allah!"

Ahlam continued to scrutinize her classmates' faces one by one. "Do they all feel the happiness that I feel?" she asked herself. "Are they all thinking what I am thinking? Did they suffer as I did to reach this moment of joy?"

The murmurings of the students and guests were silenced by the mistress of ceremonies. "In the name of Allah, the beneficent, the merciful," she announced. "May peace and blessing of Allah be upon the Prophet Mohammed, peace be upon him. Praise be to Allah who honors us with the guidance of Islam and grants us the grace of knowledge and awareness."

Silence overwhelmed the crowded hall. This was the moment they had long waited for. The commencement moved slowly, with orations about the march of knowledge, until the audience began to clap happily. Each woman in the audience felt as if she had a thousand daughters and a thousand sisters waiting to be embraced and congratulated with, "May Allah grant you every success."

Ahlam cast her eyes over the crowd and she, too, felt as if they all had come to honor her and wanted to embrace her. The whole world seemed to rejoice in her success. She trembled as she waited for her name and grade to be announced.

* * *

Long ago she had felt this way. But no, it was different. She was eleven years old then, and waiting for her name to be announced on the radio as one of those who had graduated from elementary school. Hope and expectation had filled her heart—but only until the day before graduation, when her father told her mother, "Listen, that certificate is enough for Ahlam. It is not necessary for her to continue her studies. She must learn housework to help you, help herself, and save us the trouble of schools."

Who would have thought that a father's decision would

shatter such happy dreams and rosy expectations? Ahlam's ambitions, perseverance, and innocence were shaken. Who was she, she wondered. She knew herself by the response she had received from her classmates, teachers, principal, and by her own response to her books, and by her name, which was always first in the examination scores: Ahlam Saeed was first in her class. She knew herself in her kind mother's prayerful wish that she continue her education until she became a great professor. Separated from school, who was she then?

Her mother and aunts tried to persuade her father to let Ahlam pursue her studies, but they failed. Everyone who had expected a bright future for her was disappointed; all dreams and expectations had collapsed. Her father had given his decision. When her name was announced, tears fell from her eyes, tears of sadness and pain.

Ahlam lived through five years without a course of study to challenge her intellect, without classmates, without exams or exam results to wait for. Yet she read and thought about whatever she came across. She encouraged her brothers and younger sisters to ask her assistance with their homework, and helped them gladly even when they said they hated their classes. She read her elder brothers' books; she memorized poetry and studied Islamic jurisprudence. Whenever one of her brothers was puzzled by mathematical problems or theories, she helped with joy, solving difficult problems in algebra and calculus. She asked relatives and neighbors about school news and studies, to feel herself closer to classrooms, teachers, and classmates. She amazed everyone around her. How could such a thing happen?

So the five years did not make her forget the academic world that she loved, though her pain was doubled whenever the results came out. She was distressed by what she missed: time was passing and she remained in her dark corner, pondering her sadness. Yet she dared not stand in front of her father and endure his harshness.

"Oh, Mother," she would plead, "please ask him to give me a chance, to reconsider! When can I return to school? I am almost dying of eagerness. Everybody is racing with time, and I have no hope except the mercy of Allah, which I hope will put me back on course so I can feel the freshness of life as other people do. Oh, Mother, please."

"Oh my darling, I wish I could. I've tried many times, but

nothing has changed. He has even told me not to talk about it any more. Do you understand? He believes that girls don't need degrees but should learn the practical things that are useful for their marriages. I've told you this many times."

"Well then, I'll talk to him. Yes, today. I can't be passive any longer! I need to know what he is thinking. Why did he make this unjust decision? I will convince him, mother. Then I will go back to school, inshallah."

She wiped the tears from her cheeks and prayed, "Ya Allah, help me!"

* * *

"Good evening, Father. May I be seated? I want to talk to you about something serious."

She said these words with surprising confidence, looking into his face. She didn't know that she could face her father like that; she had never tried. None of her brothers or sisters ever talked to him at all, except through their mother. His curtness was legendary.

"Good evening, Ahlam. Do sit. You want to discuss returning to school! Well, I heard you talking to your mother a while ago. Am I not right?"

"Yes, Father. And I hope that you'll tell me why you have not wanted me to study. Being in school not only gives me the chance to learn in a systematic way, it also lets me know all types of people, in a learning community. Education is an Islamic necessity! Knowledge is a necessity! And schools have become the most important means of spreading knowledge! Believe me, Father, the school is a world of goodness. Our teachers are like our mothers, and the administrators are like our fathers sending their pupils to deal with Allah and the world in better ways."

"Ahlam, my daughter, I have been aware of what you're saying, but I've waited for you to say it, waited for this attitude to come from your side. I must also confess that I made a mistake by putting myself into a shell and dragging you along with me. I thought that being in a shell deep in the sea would protect you from the current, and I wanted you protected."

"Father, hasn't the time come for us to get out of the shell and see the real world— its seas and its shores?"

"Yes, Daughter, it's time to do so. We have been so late."

Ahlam's recollections were interrupted by the voice of the announcer; "Ahlam Saeed Mansoor. The grade is Honors with Highest Distinction."

The hall was filled with applause, and the sound carried her from the world of memory into the world of the present. When she reached for her diploma, her eyes embraced all those in front of her and she heard a kind sound that shook her. "Look, Sister, that's my daughter, Ahlam!"

Her eyes filled with tears, but this time they were tears of joy.

Note

1. 'Universities with programs for female students are found in many of the major cities in the Saudi kingdom. Taught by an exclusively female faculty, girls can pursue studies in most areas with the exception of engineering.

Why Shouldn't I Be Like Her?

Jamilah Fatani

A stepmother can cause her unfortunate stepchild unbearable pain, especially when the father is unwilling to become involved in parental responsibility. In such cases it should be the father's role to ensure just treatment of all his children, but in this story the little stepsister is the only adult.
—Editors

Muneerah whispered softly like the chirping of a bird that spreads sweet melodies and warmth, "Oh Dalal, would you like to share my food? Come on, let's eat together and play together, too. I've always wanted us to share everything. Wouldn't you like that?"

Dalal nodded her head and looked around her as if she were afraid of saying something so bad that it would take her life. She blinked and then closed her eyes to prevent the rain of tears from falling, because that rain always brought suffering to her sister. Muneerah was her only hope of warmth, warmth that embraced her whenever their eyes met, or whenever they had a few moments far away from the eyes of Umm Muneerah, Muneerah's mother, or whenever they were apart but their spirits flew together.

But the pain of cruel injustice was almost more than the twelve-year-old Dalal could bear. She had spent most of those years in a joyful, rosy nest that sheltered her and her own mother. Yes, she missed the love of her father who had left eight years ago, but she enjoyed the warmth of her mother's wings and the satisfying freedom when her own wings touched the sky. Her mother had fed her lovingly. She would never forget the tears that ended the happiness. The anguished looks that scattered all kinds of questions with no answers. Why do we have to separate?[1] When will we see each other again? How will we live, far apart? Will my father let me throw seed on the road so I can find my way back to this nest? Or will the wind erase all traces of my path? Oh, Mommy! Oh, Mommy!

Dalal felt Muneerah's hand touch hers and heard her warm whisper beg, "Dalal, don't you want to share with me? Don't you want to?"

Dalal asked sadly, "But how can we do what we want? If your mother knew of our dreams she would kill them before they were even born. Maybe you have the right to dream, but your mother doesn't give me that right. Even if I just dared to dream it, she would pluck out my nails and clip my wings."

"Don't worry," Muneerah said, "she is in her room, asleep. I made sure of that, believe me. I know I am being bold, but don't worry. I will take any blame. I'm the one who is bringing the food, not you."

Muneerah led Dalal to her room. How different the girls' rooms were! Muneerah had lived in hers all her life and was used to it, but to Dalal it was a powerful reminder of her other world—not the corner of the storage room where she slept now, but her room in her mother's house: two almost duplicate pictures. The white rug, like her gold one, the red curtain like her flowered one, the pictures on the walls. Dalal stared at a picture that expressed kindness and warmth: a small bird in a nest on a green branch, opening her mouth to receive a seed from the loving mother bird. The same picture had hung in her room in her mother's house—yes, the same picture, painted with the same brush, in the same colors, on the same paper, and with the same frame around it. It even hung the same distance from her own curtain.

Again, Muneerah's voice brought her back to reality. She had laid out dishes of food on a newspaper on the floor. "Dalal, come here, sit down," she said, and Dalal embraced her call as thirsty land embraces rain.

"You will not eat our leftovers as my mother would have you do. I will do the impossible and have her treat us equally. The most important thing is that we stay together, that I can share everything with you and you share everything with me. Everything, both joys and tears."

Dalal shook and said in low tearful voice, "No, Muneerah. I

don't want you to share my tears and suffering. No, I don't." Tears dropped from her eyes. Her step-mother's cruelty and her father's negligence had erased the twelve-year-old's cheerfulness and made tears her main feature.

"Oh, Dalal," said Muneerah, "how great are these pieces of food that we eat together! Even if they were leaves from trees, they would be more delicious than the grilled ducks and pigeons that I eat with my parents but without you."

Umm Muneerah's voice rang loudly through the house. "Where are you, Dalal? Come set the table, your father is here!"

Dalal folded the newspaper with the food that was left. She intended to run to obey her stepmother, but she couldn't; she shivered with fear, and when her stepmother's curses and beating began to fall upon her thin body, she couldn't breathe.

"There was nothing else left for you to do wickedly except to steal food!" shouted Umm Muneerah. "Oh, Abu Muneerah, father of Muneerah! Come look at your daughter. She has turned into a thief!"

Muneerah ran to her mother and took her hands, saying with a quivering voice, "No, Mother! I am the one who brought the food for both of us. My sister is not a thief. I swear to Allah, I was the one who brought the food. I have always wanted to share my food with her. But I never dared to ask for that to happen."

Her mother started to beat Dalal again, shouting, "You've fooled my poor daughter to save yourself from punishment. You tricked her to bring you our food so that you would not be called a thief. Thief and liar!"

Muneerah shook like a terrified bird but ventured, "Mother. No, Mother! I was the one who brought the food, who wanted to bring it, who thought of bringing it! Why aren't you blaming me? Punish me, Mother, if that was a crime. Why don't you beat me the way you beat her? Why don't you make me suffer like her?"

The surprised look on Umm Muneerah's face met the unconcerned looks of the father who had paused for a moment in the doorway. Her voice rose a higher pitch as she shouted, "What is this, Muneerah? Are you a masochist who likes to suffer?"

"No, Mother," said Muneerah, "but I love my sister Dalal. And I would like you to be just, and have peace of mind."

"What are you saying? I can't understand a thing. You want me to make you suffer? To clip your wings and pull out your nails in order to get peace of mind? Oh, Allah! What do I hear?"

Muneerah moved with confused steps toward Dalal and said, "Oh, Mother. I won't let you beat or insult Dalal ever again. I'll bear all of it for her. You must let us share our lives. She is my sister!"

"But Dalal should learn to be polite. She was badly brought up. That is why I punish her."

"No, Mother, that is not why you make her suffer. It is because another bird brought her to your nest. What if a wind some day throws me out to another nest? Wouldn't you be sad if an eagle pulled out the nails of your poor bird?"

"Why are you interfering? What is the use of all of this talk?"

"Mother, in the law of birds, no bird will leave her sister to run away if an eagle or wild cat attacks the nest. They live or die together. How would you feel if an eagle attacked only me, and my sisters ran away and left me alone?"

Umm Muneerah closed her eyes, sat down on the bed, and brushed tears off her cheeks. Then with her eyes still closed, she spread her arms. She opened her eyes to find the two, Muneerah and Dalal, in her lap. Umm Muneerah embraced both girls and murmured, "No, my love, you'll not be taken to another nest. And you, Dalal, will be my bird, too. You can go visit your mother and then you can decide to stay with her, but you can also live peacefully here with us. If you decide to stay with us, you and Muneerah will share everything. Who knows, maybe you will get even more love here than Muneerah, and she will be jealous of you?"

They all laughed. Muneerah looked happily at her sister and said, "No, Mother, all we want is justice and your peace of mind."

Note

1. In the case of divorce, it is customary that children over the age of twelve reside with their father, who is their legal guardian.

Zainab

Sharifah ash-Shamlan

Zainab is a woman full of hope and love whose individuality is not recognized. Her marriage offers her only material comforts, which cannot substitute for respect. When she disappears, her relatives and friends wrongly suspect her of immoral acts, only to discover otherwise.
—Editors

Zainab had not gathered together her things. She had left everything as it was. At two in the afternoon her husband woke up to find his room as it was yesterday: his ashtray full of cigarettes, his coffee cup dirty, his shoes and socks where he'd left them. The house swam in silence.

Nobody knew where Zainab was. He asked for her at her parents' house and at her friends' houses.

"Zainab, where are you?" he asked himself. He went to his office and tried not to worry; only when absorbed in his work could he forget her for a while.

Her mother put on her *abayah*, wrapped her scarf around her hair, and went out with her driver to search for Zainab under the pretense of routine visits.

Zainab's maternal aunt said, "I saw her yesterday evening. She didn't say anything serious, but she looked depressed."

Her paternal aunt wet her lips and said, "Oh, I haven't seen her for two weeks. She must be preoccupied with something."

The *murdi'*, Zainab's old nanny, had been at her son Ahmed's house early that morning and remembered seeing her there.

Ahmed said, "She came to see me and I offered her the rent money for her house in the middle of the town."

Zainab had left home: it was a fact everyone agreed upon.

"Look for her passport." It was there.

"Search for her ID card." But she didn't have one of her own; she was included on her husband's card.

Her eldest brother put his head between his hands and said, "I'll kill her when we find her."

Her younger brother mumbled, "But the most important thing is to find her."

Her youngest sister was afraid.

Her husband was finally obliged to telephone the police, who promised to carry out a quiet, thorough search.

In despair, her mother slapped herself and said, "I know her, she is restless. I'm sure she has done something to herself. I wish I'd never given birth to her."

The husband looked down at his shoes and repeated, "It was a black day when I married her. She wants to work, but what for? Then she wants to join charities. Isn't it enough for her just to give money away to the poor? Always restless."

Her old nanny cried incessantly and asked her son, "Did she tell you what to do with the rent money?"

He stared at the floor and said, "No." He didn't want to tell the others that she had told him to use it to repair his house, and keep the rest for his children.

They searched one house after another, determined to find her. Whatever Zainab had done, they kept telling each other, she would not bring shame to her family.

They asked the servants one by one.

The driver said, "I didn't take her anywhere."

The children's nanny said, "I didn't see her after she gave me instructions concerning the children."

The maid said, "I didn't see her after she gave me a hundred riyals yesterday morning."

The cook said, "I haven't seen her since I served her breakfast yesterday."

Where was Zainab? The question troubled everyone. Her mother tied her head with cloth and tried to remember old neighbors and friends Zainab might have gone to.

The husband thought, "She must be with . . . HIM." He knocked on the door violently. A small girl, blowing a bubble with her gum, opened the door.

"Who are you, my little one?"

"I'm the daughter of the owner of this house."

"What is your father's name?"

She told him. He hit his forehead with his palm. The man was married, with children. He must have forgotten Zainab, even if she had not forgotten him.

The scandal was ringing the doorbell at that house. His sons' wives and daughters' husbands should not hear a thing about this.

His smaller children had gone to school, their faces filled with questions about their mother's sudden departure. The house returned to deep silence.

The cook entered the storage room to search for something in the large freezer. Zainab was inside the freezer. She had frozen into a mannequin of ice.

Who closed the freezer door on Zainab?

But that is another matter.

The Duties of a Working Wife
Wafa Munawwar

Education brings Laila, a "new Saudi Arabian woman," success in both her home and her profession. The demands of her profession, in addition to the demands of home management, housework, and parenting, are exhausting. Yet it is through these multiple roles that the "new woman" is born.
—Editors

It is after midnight, and all the members of this family are deep asleep, all the rooms are dark, and silence overwhelms the house except in two rooms. One is inhabited by darkness but the high sound of snoring comes from it, tearing the silence of night and filling the apartment with its continuous nuisance.

Laila, housewife and mother of four, tries to coordinate her home duties with her duties as a teacher. She does not admit that her responsibilities can be too much to bear. She believes that these are duties to be fulfilled so that both her home life and her professional life can be stable and happy. It was the only condition she stipulated in her marriage contract: to be able to teach.[1] She and Mahmoud have agreed upon that. So she can't be negligent but must carry out the duties of a housewife and a teacher responsibly. And if some day she feels unable to continue her work, she will quickly withdraw from her profession to concentrate on homemaking.

She is still awake preparing new lessons for tomorrow. Layers of thick, colored paper lie all over the floor; the lesson plan is open, for she is still writing the application examples, and hasn't yet finished the religious objectives for the class. Around her are seven nylon sacks of seed, examples of agricultural exports. Green cards present questions, yellow cards present answers.

Nearby, a small radio plays an Arab song with sweet and kind words. She tries to kick drowsiness from her eyes by softly singing along.

Finally she completes her work and goes to the kitchen to put what she has cooked for tomorrow into the refrigerator. Getting ready to sleep, she makes sure that the alarm is set. She surrenders her fatigued body onto the bed. Mahmoud continues to snore, disturbing the still of the night.

* * *

Laila likes to arrive at school early; delays annoy her. She has never been late. She knows what Mahmoud thinks while he drives, and turns her head away from his inquiry. She covers her face with her veil, letting her eyes disappear under the black gauze. It is not yet time for her to quit. She is not tired and has worked too hard to master her career to give up now.

Traffic lights delay them. Whenever he wakes up late, the traffic lights sleep. Eventually they get the older children to their schools and the baby to her mother. Today all her classes have new lessons, except for the group that is taking a test. She will use that time to correct homework. She hopes to get there before the principal has closed the attendance file.

A sudden red light—for the fifth time. Mahmoud slams on the brakes jolting her forward, and then laughs.

"You're the reason I am late today! Do you think it's funny? I almost hit the windshield!"

"I'm sorry. You still have fifteen minutes, that gives you enough time to prepare for work."

An idea forms in Laila's head. When she returns home, she'll go straight to bed and sleep. But how can she, when the clothes need ironing? And she'll have to go over her children's homework, tend to her husband's needs, the cries of her baby—and find time to correct the exams!

Her soliloquy is interrupted by her husband: "Isn't it about time for you to retire? What do you think? How about quitting the end of this year?"

"Ilhamdillah! Thanks to Allah! We've reached the school and there's no time to answer you—anyway, you already know my answer."

At the administrative office, Laila sits hugging her students' notebooks as she listens to her supervisor say, "The lesson was 100 percent successful. Your grasp of the material is excellent, your teaching method is attractive, and you kept the students' attention. Your learning aids fulfilled their objectives. But your voice was somehow low, perhaps due to the large room? May Allah help you and crown your efforts with continuing success. I congratulate your headmaster for having a teacher of your caliber in the school!"

Laila smiles quietly. She says, "Thank you for your kind words. I am just doing work that interests me. It makes me proud."

Laila then stops by the teachers' room, where she can sit down for the first time since the day began. Some of her colleagues are drinking tea. She remembers there's chalk dust on her hands and leaves to wash. When she just starts to sip some tea, the school bell rings for the beginning of the next class. She continues to sip; she has no class, it is her break. But it seems she will not enjoy that: one of the other teachers has influenza, and Laila has to substitute. One day she might need a similar sacrifice from her colleague.

* * *

On the way home, they pick up the children. Once in the door, Laila drops her *abayah* on the floor as she rushes toward the bedroom to put her youngest in his cradle. One of her sons cries with hunger, so she rushes to prepare a late lunch. As she passes the laundry room, she turns on the washing machine.

During the meal, the telephone rings. No one volunteers to answer it, so she finds herself obliged to do that. Suddenly her youngest cries, so she quickly finishes the conversation and hurries to the bedroom with a bottle. She knows what woke him: Mahmoud has finished eating and rushed to sleep after his long day of hard work. He has not even finished reading the newspaper headlines, so those stay on his sleepy face.

Dear friends will be her guests in the evening, so she starts to prepare for their visit. Time passes quickly; she hears the *muezzin's* call to prayer.

* * *

Her home is full of guests. Laila, they think, is elegant: the most beautiful wife, the most successful, the most able to manage her home single-handedly. She is to be envied. Laila searches for her husband's usual questioning look but does not see it; perhaps he recognizes her determination.

"No" to retirement. After the guests have left, Laila thinks to clean up the apartment; then she remembers that her oldest son has not done his homework, and in addition, he needs to go to the dentist tomorrow. When the TV announcer reads tomorrow's program, Laila is surprised to hear that it is Thursday, the beginning of the weekend. She takes a deep breath and relaxes with great joy. Mahmoud whispers in her ear, "The guests are returning tomorrow, to spend the weekend with us. Will you need anything from the supermarket?"

She says with a great smile, "They are welcome, may Allah salute them. We do not need anything, we have everything, dear. I took care of all that when you were sleeping and I've already prepared a great meal for them that will please you. Now I think it is clear that it is not yet time for me to retire. Agreed?"

"Agreed," he answers.

Note

1. Islamic marriage is not based upon an exchange of vows, but rather a contract that sometimes specifies certain conditions for each partner. In this case the wife has specified that she has the right to teach. Her husband agreed when he signed the contract.

Complete Calm

Sharifah ash-Shamlan

This story presents the image of the self-assured, proud, and dignified Saudi woman. Flying to the United States for a college education, Fatimah has high hopes and dreams. Though her society still insists that she have a male guardian, Fatimah demonstrates that she has the judgment and courage to be her protector's protector.
—Editors

Most of the passengers are sleeping; the flight is long. Fatimah's eyes refuse to sleep; she watches her "little" brother sleep beside her, his thick hair disheveled. How many times did she pull his hair and play with it when he was a child? But now Ahmed is a man, the man who is giving her the opportunity to accept the scholarship by accompanying her to America—by being her *mahram*, her male relative who must protect her safety and welfare, and who could thus obtain her exit visa.

"Protect her safety and welfare," even though he will be living in a state a thousand miles from where she will study. How she wishes to live with him, in order to take care of *him*! Then he could always come home to clean clothes and good meals, and she could spoil him the way their mother, rahimaha Allah—Allah bless her soul, used to. But he is no longer a child; let him live his life. She smiles in the dark. Too often she forgets that he is her *mahram*, she is not his. As he likes to tease: "Fatimah, I think that they made a mistake. You should be my *mahram*, not the opposite."

Two passengers in her row are flattering each other. Maybe they're on their honeymoon. Maybe they, too, have scholarships. Or maybe the husband has the scholarship, because for so many young men, a scholarship to an American school is a visa for taking along his young wife—who cares what happens later?

The plane shakes a little. Fatimah is used to this but the newlyweds are frightened and they pray and recite some *surahs*[1] from the Quran. Fatimah smiles. "Goddamn air pockets. They interrupted their beautiful moment!" she says.

Her brother opens his eyes, "What time is it?"

"Four more hours. Go back to sleep."

He puts his arm over his head and goes back to sleep.

A tiny girl comes to Fatimah, extends her hand and says, "Mama!" Her heart jumps. What a sweet word! She has never been addressed as "Mama." Her forced marriage fifteen years ago did not give her the opportunity to be a mother. Fatimah lifts the girl to her lap, but the child discovers that Fatimah is not her Mama and runs away, looking for her mother.

The airline hostess passes by and rather immodestly seats herself beside a man wearing Arab clothes. Their heads come close, and they whisper. "Adam does not make her responsible for his sons,"[2] Fatimah thinks. She remembers seeing the man in the Dhahran airport, and even there he looked familiar. She imagines him without the beard and mustache, which are decorated with some gray hairs; then she sees him as a young man passing in front of her family's house to glimpse her older sister. "So, he has become old and grown that beard," she thinks, and smiles, imagining him as her brother-in-law.

She is thirsty and goes to the bar for water. Three men stand there drinking cocktails. "Whisky smells dreadful," she thinks. "But this is none of my business." As she takes a paper cup and pours water, one of the men puts his arm around her waist. Coolly she raises the cup and pours water over his head. His friends laugh. He lets go and looks ashamed. She can't believe she acted with such calm. Again she pours water into her cup and drinks, then returns to her seat. She hopes she looks calm, but there is fire in her chest. "If women really have less intelligence and religion than men," she thinks, "then most of the men must lose theirs by choice. Most women's intelligence is greater than their experience and that strengthens and deepens their religion." She forces a smile. "Oh, yes, men are the masters. They are everything, whether I like it or not."

She takes out the book she bought at the airport. She knows from the title that it's silly: *Coffee, Tea, or Me*. She doesn't like to read anything serious when traveling. Turning on the light she browses through its chapter titles and cartoons. One part is "Adventures in the Sky for Two Airline Hostesses." No. She turns off the light and amuses herself with her thoughts.

Tomorrow she'll arrive in Denver. She'll stay with her brother in the hotel. She knows Denver well, its streets, buildings, and parks; she earned her bachelor's degree there four years after she was divorced from her cousin. She will buy a house. She has tried living in a university dormitory and found it unbearably disgusting. She will buy a used car—no, maybe a new car, for the warranty? But if she buys a car, she might not be able to buy a house. And the house is important, that cannot be delayed, because she'll spend five years there. She'll make a down payment, and the rest of the cost will be no more than rent would be. When she finishes her doctorate she'll sell the house, so it will be as if she'd been paying nothing. Maybe she'll even make some profit.

So postpone the new car for now, though in America women drive, and she has learned how. But—furniture, other necessities? The money she received from her employers at the Ministry is not enough for both a down payment and a car. . . . Furniture is not important. A bed and a bookcase are enough ; let her cosmetics stay in her suitcase. Mostly she needs a house and a car. . . . Her dreams make her smile, and her tired eyes feel relaxed.

Her dreams stop when a hand touches her shoulder. Fearfully she opens her eyes. It's the man who put his arm around her. He stammers, "May I tell you something?"

"Go ahead." Her voice sounds coarse.

"Please forgive me. I didn't mean to bother you."

"That's all right." She tries to appear normal.

"Are you angry at me?"

"You weren't in a situation that allowed me to be angry with you."

"You mean I was drunk." He repeats, "I'm sorry, I didn't mean it."

"I told you, it's all right," she says, trying to end it.

"But I want to make sure you have forgiven me."

"By God, I forgive you. Khallas, enough."

"Am I bothering you with my talk?"

"No, never. But my brother is sleeping and I don't want him disturbed."

Withdrawing a little, he runs his hand over his hair. "I'm sorry." Then he goes away.

She twists her lips sarcastically and says to herself, "He's a nice man." She sees the hostess and the other man whispering to each other. She remembers a silly French film she saw three years ago, one she had insisted on seeing after she heard about it. She closes her eyes to avoid seeing "live" episodes from the film right in front of her. "How ugly immoral behavior is," she thinks. "This man probably has a wife who perfumed him and saw him off before he traveled; the drunken fellow, too, might have a wife whom he promised he wouldn't drink. If wives could wear hats to make them invisible, would homes still exist or would all of them collapse?" She thanks Allah for intelligence and religion.

* * *

The airplane is shaking hard, and dishes are scattered. Fatimah and the other passengers become afraid. The hostess stands up and tells the passengers to be seated, fasten their safety belts, and be calm. The lights are turned on. Muslims read short *surahs* from the Quran. Catholics make the sign of the cross. Fatimah watches despite the thudding of her heart: the drunk man has sobered and started reading the Quran, and the hostess' admirer murmurs with lipstick still on his face. A laugh escapes Fatimah's mouth. If the plane crashes, most of the passengers will die with the signs of sin on them, making it easy for the angels who examine the dead.

"Is this the moment to laugh, Fatimah?" her brother asks with a quaver in his voice.

"Ya Ahmed, a person who doesn't steal is never afraid," she laughs.

The hostess calms the passengers and apologizes. "The door to the food locker was not closed tightly and it opened, causing the plates to scatter." She apologizes for being unable to serve breakfast. Then she starts collecting the scattered plates. Fatimah finds under her seat a breakfast that is still sealed. She thanks Allah while eating. The passengers unfasten their safety belts, and some of them start moving around; the noise gets louder.

Notes

1. A chapter of the Quran.
2. I am not my brother's keeper.

To Celebrate Being a Woman

Fatimiah al-ᶜUtaybi

If appearances are superficial, then why are we measured by the way we look rather than by what we are? If being a woman is scorned, then the narrator would rather be a male. But what kind of male would she want to be? Not a defeated, good-for-nothing failure, but . . .
—Editors

Since sunlight first shone into my eyes I've wished, dreamed, that I had been born a man.

Whenever I searched my closet for the right dress to wear or wondered which of the shoes would look most elegant, I felt the lump of fear in my throat.

This contradiction spread inside me like a cancer: if outside appearances are superficial, then why are we measured by the way we look, instead of by our inner beauty?

To banish my angry chagrin I turned to my studies, picking up one of the books upon which I would be examined.

I wish I had been born a man! Then I wouldn't have to worry about the contradiction. I would simply study my lecture notes and reading notes, and waste no time looking into the mirror. I wish I had been born a man! Then I would fly down the streets in my luxurious car, far away from the smelly onion that ruins my nails, and away from the foam of soap that dries my skin.

I wish I weren't a woman. Then I could live peacefully. I wouldn't worry about the future, about leaving my family behind when I marry, without knowing what to expect.

I could relax at school, unafraid of all the things that try to kill a woman's ambitions. But as a woman, if I'm educated to higher levels, they will say that I'm arrogant; if I'm cultured, they will say that I have a psychological complex. But if I merely stay at home, they will say that my abilities are so meager that I'm unable to finish my studies.

* * *

At last I have come to accept all these accumulations. "Those who see the misfortunes of others," says the proverb, "find their own misfortunes diminished." The misfortunes of men are so grave that the taste of "I wish I were" has disappeared from my mouth. I seemed to have chewed and swallowed it with my yogurt salad.

I first realized this when I was gazing into the mirror for a long time, looking for "I wish I were" under my tongue. I even searched my toothbrush for it. But nowhere could I find even its remains. Evidently I no longer embrace the wish. No longer desperate to be a man, to be just any man, my inner self is now rejoicing that I am not!

I am finally celebrating my femininity. I have learned to celebrate being a weak creature with no demands weighing on my shoulders—demands to set up the tent of history on solid ground that does not sway underneath. No intellectual reasonings force *me* to plow the red soil looking for a green history lit with white. No swords haunt *me* in my dreams or nightmares, showering me with red blood that smells of Rabin, Shamir, and the rest. No hooves of Arabian horses crash down the walls of *my* room to make sweet sleep impossible.

I am a woman, fragile as glass!

I cannot bear harsh language. There is no pain that dwells in the pores of my skin. Even the sight of an injured Palestinian boy's blood on the street where he threw rocks at the soldiers gives me no pain. I smell my own blood's transformation—from a block of ice in the winter of Najd,[1] to the cheap funeral incense lit by the sighs of bereaved mothers in Hebron, Naples, and elsewhere in the Islamic world. No pain, from any of this.

How wonderful that I was not born a man! How did I ever harbor that wish? As a man, how could I have been able to bear the pain of this slow death or face such defeat?

Revered custom prevents me from carrying arms, and saves me from suicidal attacks. But though I'm just a woman, fragile as glass, revered custom plunges me into battle through my children. I give birth to sons and then willingly give them over to the white flame of war; how lucky that women are too fragile to feel pain.

We women all marry and bear children, so many children that we forget what they look like. Like all the other women, in the labor of birthing I will try to save myself from the labor of inability, from the death of the birth of action.

But for the present, since I am a woman fragile as glass and do not yet have any children to send to war, I must be content with crying. I will cry whenever I see women's children beaten, suffering, oppressed. After that, I will run to my bed. Under my silk bedcovers, I will cry hot tears that sting my face and spoil my braids. No, not because I was born a woman do I cry and shudder, but because you, man, were born a man. I cry for your sake! Then I will sing some songs of the children of *Infitadah*, of Uprising—of those who throw one stone, then two stones.
. . .

A homeland is born in the eyes
It wipes the sand from its sandals
And it enters the kingdom of water
And opens into another horizon
That would create another epoch
And write another text.

There is the boy upon whose forehead shine all the colors of Palestine; in his hair sticks a twig that caught there while he picked olives for our breakfast after our long and comfortable sleep. And there is another boy from whose blood I drink the water of life. And there is a third boy, who brings the smell of my old dream back to surround me once again. Will I wish that I were a boy throwing a stone or two, or will I keep the lights of the wedding hall brilliantly lit to celebrate my femininity?

It's wonderful that I am a woman who can give birth to a boy, who will not misuse the language with chatter, but rather celebrate it on the edge of a sword.

He throws one stone or two stones
He cuts the snake of Israel into two
He chews the flesh of tanks
And comes to us without hands. . . .

And then his shout in Arabic, "Palestine!" will continue to glow forever, and our swords will drip blood!

Note

1. The interior region of Saudi Arabia.

The Dove Is a Woman

Nurah al-Ghamdi

This story is about passive despair. Arab women carry a great risk from men who lie, who can so easily dishonor them, while men risk little from women. Therefore tears are sometimes women's only comfort. It is no wonder that some women seek psychiatric help.

—Editors

Many women cry before they go to sleep. It is difficult for any woman to complain. Each one thinks she is the only one to spend part of her the night crying, that beautiful but tiring act. Even if one of them thought of complaining, no man would pay any attention or be sympathetic, regardless of how sensitive he might be. He would probably say, "It is a female habit, especially when the world is sleeping and daydreams start to invade their tired thoughts."

"All women cry, but for a few of them the tears have dried up, that sweet spring no longer flows." The woman's sharp voice became a little bit choked. "The doctor told me so. He said it is not strange for women to cry. What is strange is if they do not."

I moved closer to her and asked, "Did the doctor say that without knowing the reasons for crying or the percentage of time spent crying?"

She turned towards me and asked, "Can we measure crying?"

The crowded room roared with laughter. A rattling voice rose saying, "The percentage of my crying is 75 percent, but this doctor lacks experience, it seems, in defining percentages."

The laughter grew louder. Defiantly I said, "Yes, crying has percentages; consider this as a special theory. Crying could be an illness that requires extensive treatment."

The woman next to me interrupted, "What is important is that it is crying and it springs from the heart, which is the master like the sea that pushes its waves to the shores of quiet eyes." She looked towards me and asked, "Is this your first visit to a psychiatrist?"

"Yes, it is."

"What's wrong?"

"Fear, disturbing dreams, and a strange desire to cry. What about you?"

"My complaint is not very different from yours, except for one thing. Each time I visit I ask the doctor one specific question which makes him laugh and pick up the telephone. And sometimes he tells me silly jokes and finally at the end he asks me to smile. Before that he asks me for the tenth time what is my name. Look, look at that woman in the corner. She has a strange way of crying. That girl stands up and sits down more than ten times a minute."

"The clinic is full of women. Her restlessness is natural. But I'm bored," I said. "The atmosphere is depressing, and so is the smell of the hospital. I feel like I am suffocating."

"Have patience. I have been here for four hours."

"I'll go mad if I have to wait one more hour. My son is waiting for me at home. He is very young and is not used to my being away."

"Where is his father?"

"Somewhere else," I replied.

"Does that mean you are divorced?"

"For almost two years now."

"Are you considering marriage again?"

"There is a man who wants me, but I'm worried that I'll lose my son."[1]

"What sort of relation do you have with this man?" she asked. "Engagement or love?"

"The second is closer to the truth."

"Ha! Ha! Ha!"

Her laugh upset many of the women. One of them said, "People have no shame anymore."

Another one said, "Maybe it's a fit."

A third one said, "She's crazy for sure."

Some of the young girls boldly laughed with her until the laughter spread among the whole group, even the wise and mature ones. Three minutes later the room was quiet. She raised both her hands toward her pale, sharp-featured face and wiped away the remaining tears. She continued her sporadic laughter as she looked at me and said, "And do you believe him?"

I hesitated a minute before I answered her. "Sometimes I do believe him."

I felt disgusted with my doubts.

"When I doubt him I accuse myself of being mean to him, because I believe him. I believe him at night when I'm alone and my dreams carry me far. But, as soon as the sun rises and I open my eyes to its light, I find all that has passed is just a dream, nothing more. Sometimes I hate him so much that I hope I lose my memory so that he doesn't come back to my thoughts again. But why are you asking me, and who are you?"

"I . . . I . . . I'm a woman from here," she said. "Like you I learned from childhood that a man is everything to a woman and a woman is nothing without him, she is like straw in the wind. There is a common proverb in our village which says, 'For the woman the husband is a *quz*. You know what a *quz* is, the sand dune gathered by the wind, forming a pile of sand."

"And is it always like that?" I asked her.

"Poor you. Did he tell you that he will ask for your hand in marriage?"

"No."

"Did he at least hint of this?"

"No, but I'm sure that he will."

"Why haven't you asked him?"

"I'd never do that!"

"Is that some sort of idealism?"

"No, it's self-respect."

"Ah, let me warn you. There are men who lie." Then she continued, asking, "But why do men lie?"

Someone stuck her head between me and her, and whispered in a hoarse voice, "Ask the dove."

I moved my head away from my friend to allow the newcomer the chance to talk. She shook her tousled head, fixed her look on my friend, and repeated, "I said, ask the dove."

"The dove, dove. What do you mean?"

She turned her face toward the ceiling and sang some lines.

To . . . to . . . to . . . to . . . to . . . to . . .
Oh Ahmed Adawi
Bring back my comb.
Bring back my son's toy.
To . . . to . . . to . . . to . . . to . . . to . . .
Take your gold away from me.
To . . . to . . . to . . . to . . . to . . . to . . .
Oh Ahmed Adawi
Bring back my comb.

Her song was low and lonely. It stopped suddenly with the outburst of another woman banging her head at the corner of the room. Whispers spread among the women. One of the nurses intervened, then a second, then a third. Women went out and others came in. This strange head was once again inserted between me and my friend, whom I had known for moments now. My friend whispered, "I think she is mad."

The strange woman turned slowly and looked at me with her disturbed look, and said, "I am Umm Hamamma, the mother of the dove."

I stood up and stuttered, "Dove . . . dove?"

My friend thrust her hand into her purse and put some strange pills into her mouth.

"You're sick, like me and the rest of the women here. But it's wrong to use pills for therapy," I said.

But she didn't seem to hear me. "For seven years now," she said, "I've been going to many clinics and asking the doctors why men lie."

The whispering started again.

"I told you," said the newcomer. "Ask the dove."

My friend smiled, waiting for me to argue with her. But the strange head moved back to the wall and leaned on it. For a second her loud snoring filled the room. She woke up and looked around fearfully, but then she went back to sleep.

I leaned came closer to my friend and told her, "Men aren't the only ones to lie, women lie also."

She raised her hands up in the air and said loudly, "But men don't break before they're twenty, and they don't age after fifty. So it is with the men, but only women cry. I've been crying for twenty years. Do you know why? Because I fell in love with a man more than I should have. I believed him, but afterwards he drew his sword in the face of the wind and left with the dawn."

Once again the head with the unkempt hair thrust between us.

"Didn't he hear the dove?"

Silence fell over the room except for the women's nervous breathing. The footsteps of patients and doctors could be heard outside. Then the woman's lonely singing started once again.

To ... to ... to ... to
Oh Ahmed Adawi
Bring back my comb.
Bring back my son's toy.
To ... to ... to ... to ...
Take your gold away from me.
Oh Ahmed Adawi
Bring back my comb.
To ... to ... to ... to ...

I dared to ask her, "Who is Ahmed Adawi?"

She shook her head and showed her yellow teeth in a disturbed smile. "He is the dove's lover."

"The dove. You mean the bird we see on trees?"

She clasped her hands on her chest and said, "Yes, the dove. The free and weeping dove."

"How is that?"

She came closer and said, "I'll tell you. In the beginning of creation, when all the creatures were able to speak, the dove had an admirer whose name was Ahmed Adawi. The dove had a small son with wonderful feathers. She used to comb them every day, using a comb made of sunshine. It was given to her by a fortuneteller on the day her son was born. She told the mother dove to guard it well, for her son's life was linked to the comb. The dove hid the comb under her wing and embraced her son with the other. One evening, Ahmed Adawi tried to sit beside her but she refused, afraid she would lose the comb. She reproached him by saying he came from one world while she came from another, and they both must be truthful. Ahmed

Adawi became very angry, but he hid his feelings. One day he asked her to join him for a picnic by the sea and she agreed. At the beach, he took out a large necklace and asked her to bend over so he could put it around her neck. She did as he said, and his hands sneaked to the comb, pulled it from beneath her wing and threw it into the sea unnoticed. When she returned home that night she found her son dying. She moved her wings around him and was scared to find the comb missing. She rushed back to find Ahmed, but she did not find him there. She returned to her child to find him dead. Since then everything speaks except the dove, who only cries."

She bent forward, pulling at her shaggy hair, which she hid under a thick veil and whispered, "The dove is a woman."

My friend stood up, raised her hands to her eyes as if she had been dreaming and said, "Now I know."

I looked around. The room was almost empty. The clinic had closed, and the women were leaving. I followed them out repeating, "The dove is a woman."

Note

1. In Saudi society children of divorced parents usually return to the father's house when the mother remarries.

Just Give Me the Right to Dream

Fatimah al-ᶜUtaybi

> *In Saudi society a healthy and successful marriage is supposed to represent mutual agreement and a relationship between equals. Unhappy to be used merely as a bridge for male ambition, this wife finally communicates her discontent to her husband.*
>
> —Editors

Her eyes are empty. Things have lost their meanings, even their names.

In his eyes, things flower like a green field that grows and blooms and seeds; things multiply.

Her laughter is the only language she shares with him. Often she laughs with him without understanding why he's laughing. She feels the strangeness of not understanding, but it pleases her that there is something they can share, the laughing sound.

She is the wife of a doctor.

On her bureau lies her certificate with "Fourth Grade" written upon it. It proves that she reached the fourth grade. Above his bureau hang all his diplomas, from fourth grade up to doctorate.

"How lucky you are," women tell her, "married to such a highly educated man!" Everything she has is in these words. Details do not matter. He is a doctor, and that is supposed to be enough to make her lucky.

But she still dreams that there could be some kind of communication between them, that he could talk to her as other husbands talk to their wives, without causing her to stutter and feel ashamed to be by his side. And so she just avoids him.

She prepares dinner for him before he comes, to avoid sitting with him. When he calls her to join him, she moves her lips in the words that both of them are used to hearing: "Oh, I've eaten already!"

A childish satisfaction fills her when she says those words every evening. "I have eaten before you," she thinks, "but only dinner. As for everything else, I stand hungry on ruins that do not move. You run, biting the hem of your *thobe*[1] between your teeth, fighting all the things that stand in your way, moving into your future like a crowned Ph.D."

Then she returns to her anxieties, her worrying questions. "Does he see me as capable of walking? Do I own legs to walk on? A ruin like me is only good for weeping over. He fights for what he wants; I do not move."

One night, having served him, she wishes that in his mind she were capable of stepping forward. Unaware, she takes one step, and then another, and finds herself in front of him while he is eating his dinner. He smiles at her.

"Aren't you hungry?" he asks.

"No, I've beaten you to it."

"Hunger?"

"No, dinner."

"Yes, yes . . . as usual."

He stares in front of him for a long moment. When he looks toward her again, she has backed away. She is worried; she has seen from the look on his face that there is something wrong.

"So he is worried this evening," she thinks. She has been worried for the last six years. Her worries have consumed her whole, so that nothing remains. Nothing at all. But isn't she the lucky wife, the one who married a doctor?

He sits in front of her, looks into her eyes and whispers, "How long?"

Now she knows that something serious is on his mind.

"What do you mean, how long?"

"How long will I continue to be the victim of your revenge?"

"My revenge?"

"This evening, at this moment, I am declaring war on the silence that has consumed us for the past five years since our son's death. I was not the cause of his death. I was away that evening because I was working very hard to make him proud of me when he grew older."

Yes, her son who died far away from the help of a doctor. She had held him tight in her arms—until her husband, the Ph.D., came home to find him dead in her lap.

"You could have given me another child," he goes on. "But your revenge went too far."

"And you, what did you do?" she objects. "You stubbornly kept me behind you all the time. You closed all the doors on me and turned me into a body that is only good for cooking, cleaning, and wiping for you. You never thought of holding my hand so that I could be a conscious being like you, to walk beside you. I might have gone far in my revenge, but you went farther in yours. You enjoyed being the intellectual next to my ignorance, being everything while I am nothing.

"No. If I had given in to your desire to have another child, he would have died of your neglect, or at least would be growing up incomplete. Lost between an intellectual father and an illiterate mother. Between a parent who races with the wind, building the future, and the one who waits behind the wall of silence, looking at nothingness, without awareness, without dreams. Even the dream of motherhood has died in my heart."

"Let me dream," she continues, "Give me your hand. Only you can erase these accumulated black memories. Give me my dream so that I can give you yours."

Note

1. The long white robe worn by Arabian men.

PART TWO
Social Issues

The Loss

Khayriyyah as-Saqqaf

A woman who lacks love and protection from her family and marriage is easily deceived. Abused and impoverished in her marriage, Sa'ada gives her trust to the wrong person.
—Editors

Oh! I have been here since yesterday with all these women talking about their mistakes. Each one remembers the error that brought her to this place, but why was I brought here? I just don't know.

A while ago I thought maybe I should just try to sleep. I put my *abayah* under my head and stretched out on the floor in one of the corners of the women's prison. Noise, crowds, loud laughs, women eating *fis fis* seeds and spitting out the shells.

Even in the prison they practice that dirty habit, and they gossip about others. But I can't sleep here. I've tried turning, squirming into this position and that. I'm sitting here with my arms around my legs, resting my chin on my knees and trying to follow the other women with my eyes.

One of them approached me a while ago and asked, "What is the matter with you? You have been silent since you first got here." She put her hand on my back and smiled, "In a day or two you'll be used to this life here."

Even the laughter of the women is vague and dark, like everything else in front of me. Their laughter sounds like the hissing of snakes from the darkness of the unknown. I'm shivering. Why was I brought here? Why have I been condemned to misery? Poverty? Loss?

* * *

I was searching, yesterday, through a pile of clothes for the medicine that I have to take every day, and I'd just found it when there was loud knocking on the door. When I opened the door, I was surprised to see a man in police uniform.

"Does Sa'ada Abdu live here?" he asked.

"I am she."

"I have orders to search this place."

"But why, Sir?"

"You are accused of possessing drugs."

"Drugs. Oh, no! Sir Policeman, may Allah forbid! I don't have any drugs. Oh, that can't be, I don't own any of that. . . ." Then, realizing that my reputation and my dignity were at stake, I became angry. "Oh, welcome, welcome!" I told him. "Go ahead, search the house!"

"Get out of my way, and wait right where you are."

The policeman searched all three rooms, and the neglected terrace, the trash-filled storage area, and the kitchen, which I hadn't noticed was dirty until that moment.

"I'm sorry it's so dirty," I ventured.

"Do you have any pills?" the officer shouted at me.

"Well, of course, I have my medicine."

"Show it to me, then!"

"Here."

He looked at it, looked at me, and said, "You are under arrest!"

"Why? You didn't find anything, Sir. What am I to do with that old blind man sitting by the door? And what about the children, who is going to take care of them?"

"It's your own fault. You'll just have to face the consequences."

* * *

My fault? What have I done? Who accused me? Why am I here?

Medicine, sleep, inability to stand up. But no, my medicine couldn't be drugs. I'm shivering. I shake my head, to banish the idea. But why not? When I take my pills, I go to sleep. And I want to take them every day. I want to take my medicine. It calls me before I call it.

* * *

The day my husband divorced me he stole all I had. Not only my jewelry. He forged my signature and robbed me of my house, my clothes, my dishes, teapot, my comb, every item. Then he pulled me to the door by the hair, and pushed me out into the street, with nothing.

Crazed, I hurried to Hamidah's house—Hamidah, the old woman who always found medicine to cure the people in our quarter. When I pounded on Hamidah's door, it was as if she had been expecting me. Hamidah opened her door to me, rubbed my shoulder as I wept, wiped my bleeding face, and covered me where my dress was torn at my breast. She brought me a glass of water and some tablets to take. "These will lessen your headache." I swallowed them gratefully. "Don't worry, Sa'ada," Hamidah went on, "Allah has helped you. I have a house for you, and a husband for you. But now, sleep a while, then we'll talk about your future."

Astonished, I thought, "Hamidah always tries to comfort people. She just wants to make me feel better, to please me with some sort of hope."

I did sleep. And Hamidah offered me more of the pills when I awoke, and then each evening and morning for some days and nights. They helped me forget my disaster and my worries.

Then one day Hamidah pointed out, "This medicine is expensive, Sa'ada; and since you need more, you will have to pay its price. I am a poor woman, and you'll have to help me get your medicine."

"But how? Where do I get the money? I don't own even one piece of money, or gold, or even paper! I wouldn't even have a cloth to cover my naked body, were it not for you, who have showered me with charity!"

Hamidah didn't smile. In a serious, sharp voice she said, "Ya Sa'ada, there is no doubt that I am like a mother to you, so this is your home. But you can see the pressure of my responsibilities and expenses, especially the expenses of clothes and medicine. Don't worry about your food and shelter, because you can eat from my food and shelter with me, but. . . ."

"Oh, what can I do? I owe you so much!"

"I have a husband for you, my dear. I think you should accept him. He has a house, and he has a little money, and he has small children who need a mother."

"Small children?" Children are my eternal point of weakness. I had no children of my own from my marriage, but when my neighbor died I took care of her two boys. But my husband deprived me of them, as well as everything else.

Hamidah shook me. "Sa'ada! Where was your mind wandering? What do you say? Will you marry him?"

"Oh. Of course," I told her, "of course. I agree."

* * *

I married him, and on that day was surprised to find out that he was blind, though he had pretended to be able to see. He did own a tiny house, but that was all, and he could not do any work. The children really did need care, so I found work as a servant in others' homes to provide food for them, and him, and myself.

One day when I felt unbearably lonely, nervous, and exhausted, I went to Hamidah. "I need more medicine! I have a few coins."

But Hamidah told me she didn't have any more of it, and directed me to her neighbor, Falih. "He has some, I know."

I knocked on his door; he opened it and looked at me intensely. Then he stretched his hand out, grasped my *abayah,* and pulled me inside. He came close to me, surrounded me with his strong hands, and squeezed me. I screamed, but he would not let me go until he had the price of the medicine. He forcibly kissed me and penetrated me.

When I gathered the end of my dress, he handed me a large number of the pills. I threw them in his face and ran from his house. At home I was ashamed to look at my face in the mirror.

After sunset Hamidah came to my door and handed me the medicine. "Free of charge," she said. When I refused, it she smiled and said, "You need it today more than any other day."

* * *

I look at the women in prison and sigh deeply. How many of them are like Hamidah? How many are like me?

Saffron

Fatimah ad-Dawsari

This story dramatizes the impact that a Saudi woman can have on her community and illustrates women's important role in Saudi Arabian philanthropy. When a woman's money is her own, the Quran encourages her to do charitable deeds. Her own life might be enriched.

—Editors

Most of the faithful praying in the mosque left, taking different paths to return to their work. The frail old *sheikh* came out hurrying toward the market, panting. He prepared himself for another round, stopping for a moment near one of the walls and unfolding the roll of cloth that wrapped his small carton. He placed the cloth, then the carton, on the ground. Then he reached into his pocket and took out some *riyals*, counted them, and murmured, "Twenty *riyals* left! Ya Allah!"

He picked up his carton and cloth and started another round inside the *souq*, calling out in his tired, sad voice, "Saffron[1] . . . oh ladies, saffron."

Down the street in front of him, memories ran ahead of his steps, memories of years of running after each piece of bread. Life was harsh in the old days, too, despite its simplicity. He remembered his small village, the farm, the sheep, the mountain. He could even smell the fragrance of the soil and rain.

His daydreams were interrupted by a voice: "How much is the saffron, sir?"

"The small box is five *riyals*, the large one is ten r*iyals*."

Reality was totally different from the vanished memories.

He observed the man in front of him examining one of the small boxes of saffron.

"Are you buying, son?"

The man smiled obnoxiously for a moment, then touched his pocket and strode away.

The *sheikh* rearranged the small boxes to resume his rounds.

"Saffron . . . saffron, oh ladies."

The *souq* became crowded, with no room for memories. Time passed quickly. His eyes watched the hands of passersby, hoping to find one who would take some small boxes, paying their price. He wished he owned one of the big shops filled with customers. Again he anchored on the shore of memories and could hear his small grandson's voice: "Listen, my grandfather. When I grow up, I'll open a big store for you to sell saffron!"

The voice took him so far away that he collided with a passerby. He woke up to the scolding of a man with a filthy tongue who called him names. He faced the man in staring silence.

Sadness was clearly etched in the face of the tired old *sheikh*. He turned with a jerk. He looked in all directions and could hear the mingling of voices both low and high. Time was passing quickly, and no one was buying saffron.

He could see the face of his grandson waiting for him at the doorstep of their house, searching his hands, hoping to see his grandfather carrying the gym suit that he had asked for a week ago.

"Oh, my son, time is running out," he would have to say. "Tomorrow is your gym class, and no one is buying saffron." He felt something stinging in his knee and his legs were trembling from the whirl of his turning. "No, I will not stop. . . . I must sell. . . . Ya Allah!"

He looked at the sporting goods shop across the street. In front, many kinds of clothes in many colors, many sizes, were displayed. The perfect gym suit for his small grandson was there. Two days ago he had asked its price, and the owner had told him, "Thirty *riyals*."

And for two days now no one had bought any saffron. Whenever he tried to gather the amount he needed, he had to spend it on food or other necessities for home. And now he saw the tears in his grandson's eyes as he looked over his old gym suit and showed his grandmother the holes that she would try to mend.

* * *

A woman stood on the other side of the *souq*, near her maid and driver. She felt like doing something different, something to break the dull boredom of her life. Despite her riches, she was unhappy; from behind her veil, she searched for the happiness she could see on some others' faces.

An old woman passed near her. She thought the woman looked sad, so she offered her some money, but the woman refused, saying, "No, I don't need it."

Her dream of finding real happiness had almost ceased. She buried herself in the crowd, looking at storefronts, but not tempted to go inside any of them. A frail old *sheikh* passed her selling saffron, but she did not notice him.

The *muezzin*'s call to sunset prayer[2] mingled with the sounds of shops being closed and people leaving. Then she saw the old *sheikh* standing near the side of the road, and raising his hands toward the sky, murmuring words of prayer she could not hear. She came nearer to him and saw tears in his eyes.

"What is the secret behind those tears?" she wondered. Then she noticed his carton of boxes and came nearer to see what they contained.

"Saffron! I want saffron!" she called to the old *sheikh* as he began to turn down the street. "How much is the saffron, my uncle?"

He looked at her—it seemed to her hopefully—and handed her one small box. His hand was trembling.

She took the small box while studying his face. How different was his life from hers! "I'll buy all your saffron," she said. "How much do you have?"

"Bless you!" the old man said, and the *muezzin*'s voice continued the call to prayer. "Bless you!" he repeated. As the old *sheikh* moved into the mosque, she returned to her car and rode home with new feelings stirring inside her. She wished that she could look deep inside the old *sheikh*. For the first time in many days, she felt happy. She smiled. She promised herself to return to this place to buy saffron, to try to discover the secret of the *sheikh*'s tears and the secrets of other eyes that she had not yet seen.

Notes

1. Saffron is an orange-colored spice used for color and flavor in Saudi rice dishes.

2. Islam requires that the devout pray in a prescribed manner five times a day. These compulsory prayers are *salat as-fajr*, the predawn prayer; *salat al-zuhr*, the midday prayer; *salat al-'asr*, the afternoon prayer; *salat al-maghrib*, the prayer that follows sunset; and *salat al-isha'*, the evening prayer. The muezzin announces these prayers during which most places of business close until prayer time is over, which usually takes about twenty minutes.

Wednesday Night

Badriyyah al-Bishir

This story dramatizes the horror of life with an alcoholic husband and the additional complications in a traditional Islamic society in which alcohol is illegal. What is a woman's recourse when she is totally dependent upon her husband? Despite the protagonist's current predicament, even a horrid marriage is better than widowhood.
—Editors

Hai is taking fast steps like a man beating the ground mercilessly with his shoes. She is thin with a flat chest, giving the appearance of a young girl who has not reached the age of femininity.

She is wondering whether her son, Rashid, has returned from school yet with the neighbor's children. The silver rays of the afternoon sun gather over her black *abayah* and nudge the tight holes in the black headscarf that droops over her chest. The street is crowded with cars, and with children leaving school, tired from a full day of learning. One of these children gives her hand to a Filipino servant, who knots the ends of her *abayah* over her chest and pulls the small girl by her hand. The girl drags her feet.

The schoolchildren fight among themselves. They jump as high as they can. Their feet balance their small bodies as they totter between standing or falling. Hai tows her daughter behind her, that child who is not yet tired of seeing the same scene each day. Little Fatima examines the girls, their white ribbons, and the colored pictures on their school bags, carefully taking note of any shoe that has mastered its game of striking stones on the path. All the while, Hai is making calculations.

It is Wednesday, and with Thursday evening the weekend[1] will be almost over. She still needs pastry dough and a cookbook to prepare a special meal for the weekend.

Rashid is waiting in front of the door playing happily with colored cards. When his younger sister enters, he pulls her braid. She screams sharply to draw her mother's attention. Hai hits her and scolds, "Didn't I tell you more than once not to scream like that?"

Fatima shouts again, "But he's the one who pulled my braid!"

Hai answers, "I'll cut your hair so that we'll have peace from your screams. Is that what you want?"

Fatima's eyes fill with annoyed astonishment, and Rashid's eyes shine with triumph. But he watches his mother's hand, fearing it might get him too.

At 5:00 p.m. every Wednesday, Hai wakes up from her nap, walks to the living room, and tries to do all of the things that she knows will be to no avail. She says, "Come on, everyone, bring your books and sit down next to me."

"But it's Wednesday, it's the weekend!" says Rashid, who has started to ride his bicycle near the front steps.

Fatima watches her mother and brother. As the moment passes without violence, she pulls her doll by its hand and follows to watch her brother and his friends race to the other end of the neighborhood on their bicycles.

Hai does not know why she asks the children to study when the weekend has just begun. She picks up the phone and dials Sheikha's number, but no one answers. She remembers that Sheikha goes to al-Kharaj every Wednesday and does not come back until Friday. She brings the teapot and a dish of spicy nuts with her, turns on the TV, and starts to watch cartoons.

She fills her first cup of tea. She sees her husband fixing his *ghutra*[2] in the mirror, pulling the two ends evenly under his chin and then placing the *igal* on top of his head. He then folds each end over the *igal*. She fills another cup as he enters the room. He takes the cup of tea and they drink silently. He takes some nuts and fills his pocket with them.

"Where are the children?" he asks as he stands.

"They are playing in the street. If you come back early, bring the bread."

"I don't think I'll come back early. I'll visit my friends when

I finish work at the office. The bakery is close by and Rashid is old enough, why not depend upon him?"

He slams the door and with it many questions slam down on her upset face. She asks herself, "Will he come back home drunk[3] as he does every Wednesday evening, mumbling meaningless things? And then start crying like a broken child, worthless as an overused shoe? Whenever he fails to win my sympathy he finds refuge in his pillow and in tears until he finally sleeps. Or else he'll fall asleep in the bathroom before he even washes his face."

She does not know if it is this drunkenness that makes her unable to love him. She picks up the tray and goes into the kitchen. She starts to make the dough for the children's dinner. They like *fatayir*[4] filled with cheese. She takes a small piece and automatically starts to make the savory turnovers.

She turns on the radio and hears a song, "You with the daring eyes."

Does she love him? She has never asked herself this question. Why does the question come up now? Is it because the song on the radio is repeating the old nonsense about love that she does not want to hear?

Why doesn't she feel love? Is it because he asks her whether she loves him or not? It has become dull. Is it because he does not ask her this question until his words are drunk and shine with tears? Then this stupid, wicked, and sad "love" appears. Why is it that "love" is not like she wanted it to be? He stole her when she was sixteen years old. Love for her then was colored papers, handwritten with many spelling errors and with quoted phrases from a *How to Write Love Letters* book she had borrowed from a friend at school.

She would just open the book and whatever page she opened to, she would copy the whole letter after "Dear love," and then sign her name after "Sincerely yours."

Then she would send her younger sister to the door in front of theirs after tipping her one *riyal*, and another when she returned. He would be there to receive the letter and give her sister one *riyal* too. The letter would come back soaked in perfume that drew mental circles on the small words.

A speeding car passes by the kitchen window, then a screeching noise fills the street like the barking of dogs and spreads fear. She quickly opens the window searching for her two small children. Some teenage boys are crossing the street, fighting among themselves, and throwing their books into the back seat of their car.

One of them notices her moving at the window, and notices the anger in her eyes. He shouts, flirting with her, "I die at the sight of such gazelle-like eyes."

She slams the window shut. Her lips move, murmuring a long prayer that Allah will quickly take the souls of such shouting teenagers who bother people with their noise and crazy car horns.

But does she really find such flirting bothersome?

Her thoughts return to her husband's doubting face. It is the eighth year of her marriage. The cold marble floor sends chills through her. This boy makes love taste cold in the heat of the night, when what she needs instead is a strong arm to hold her.

"Ya Allah. Why should I have to wait in front of the bakery for half an hour while the bread is baked?"

She looks at her watch. Why is Wednesday night so long? Is it because she is waiting for him? Because the children's homework is delayed? Because of a dinner that does not have an appointed time, because of the man who does not care when he returns? The night stretches on as she washes the doughy dishes.

Late in the night the children become sleepy in front of the soap opera. Dust from the street still hangs on the edges of their clothes. She carries them to their bedroom. How many times has she requested separate bedrooms for the boy and the girl? But he doesn't care.

"For him I am just an old-fashioned woman with a psychological complex," she thinks.

She lies down on the sofa in front of the television. She watches the made-up faces of the actresses. She calls them names and insists that it is they who seduce the minds of men. She thinks that what threatens women is this type of charm, mastered only by these whores!

She looks at the clock. It is midnight, time when he falls unconscious and the night begins to blur. When he awakes, what time will it be? What frightens her are the stories she hears about drunken men and the Islamic punishment of flogging in the public square for such men, announced on the TV every Friday.

One drunk killed another while under the influence of alcohol. Another raped a relative while drunk. A third caused a car accident and hit a mysterious body at midnight. She is afraid of becoming a widow while she is still so young. Who will provide for her children then?

She wakes up frightened by an actress shouting on the television. Did she sleep? Was she dreaming? She shouts back at the actress, as if she could hear her, "May Allah ruin your voice!" After that she turns to the clock hanging on the wall. It is one o'clock. She jumps from the sofa and begins to pace the room and the hall.

Did he run off the side of the road? Perhaps he couldn't tell the difference between a black goat and the light pole whose light is out. "Ya Allah, how the evening becomes long when he is out."

"He" always becomes that third person pronoun, even when he is present. It is "he" who rents the house, brings the groceries, "protects" them—although she is sure that no one would fear a maudlin drunk who always cries.

As she worries, her blood burns. She rubs her palms together and cracks her fingers nervously, waiting. At that moment, the sound of footsteps comes to the door, which suddenly opens as he tries with difficulty to remove the key. The smell that precedes him frightens her. Then he slams the door shut.

"Why do you cower there like a thief?" he demands.

"You have the right to say that, but do you think a thief fears a man like you? Who comes home dragging his feet?"

"Shut up!" his disturbed baby-face shouts.

She shouts some broken phrases back at him.

"You're not a man. If I hadn't been afraid of my father's stick. . . . I wish I'd never married you!"

She thinks that he will, as usual, cry at her knees.

But this time he clenches his jaw, raises his hand, and slaps her on the face. When she flinches, he kicks her and leaves.

When she hears him start the car's engine she thinks that he might drunkenly crash into the light pole and kill himself. What a tragedy it would be! She'd become a widow and her children would be fatherless. She hates living in her loveless marriage, but it is better than being a destitute widow with children.

She follows him, opens the door, and sees the car's rear lights move away from the curb. Then the car disappears.

Notes

1. Students attend school Saturday through Wednesday. Friday is the official day of Sabbath, with most businesses and governmental offices closed that day.
2. White square cloth worn by men as a headdress and held in place with an black cord known as an *igal*.
3. Alcohol is an illegal substance in Saudi Arabia.
4. A triangular-shaped turnover filled with cheese, meat, or spinach.

In a Puzzling Whirlwind

Amal ᶜAbdul-Hamid

This story stresses that a woman is more than a brood mare. It is not fertility that makes a woman worthy of respect, but her ability to become independent. Western readers will notice that everyone, including the narrator, assumes that the infertility is the woman's problem, not the man's. This is a common Arab assumption.

—*Editors*

For a long time I have tried to write about my suffering, to clarify what I have endured, but my thoughts were crippled. I wish I had the courage to break down the fences of weakness and humiliation that imprisoned me. I want to relive my past in order to rid myself of the present.

That past started when I was sixteen. My mother had raised me to depend on myself and had given me the freedom of choice.

My life's routine swung between sadness and happiness, desperation and hope. Reading made up for my lack of friends. My sisters and brothers were so much older that all attempts at communication with them were losing battles. I became a recluse, stayed in my room, and rarely went out.

Finally I found a friend in our new neighbor's daughter. Muna and I visited almost daily. Our friendship became stronger when we became classmates as well.

One day, Muna and her mother unexpectedly came to visit. My mother listened to her mother's whispers for some time. I thought perhaps they needed a loan or some other help. My guess became stronger when Mother whispered to Father. Later, Father talked to me about the matter: "Your friend's brother would like to marry you." I was surprised by the unexpected news.

My father repeated in confusion, "You are still too young and marriage is a responsibility that you might find hard to bear." I heard his words like a flame of challenge. I loved taking risks and wanted a chance to enter a new world that I had not experienced. Furthermore, I would have the opportunity to live close to Muna.

Soon I married Ahmad and moved to my new home to enjoy a life in a different world, but I was like a bird that didn't know where to land. In no time, I found myself a lonely stranger, particularly after Muna married and moved away.

A year passed and his mother began to say harsh things and to call me names. She said she wanted to see his children as she had seen those of his brothers.[1] Out of respect for Ahmad, I didn't answer back. He encouraged me and calmed my fears. But his eagerness for a child sobered me. I wanted to give my husband and his mother a child. I didn't want him to give up on me or have another woman share our marriage. It is difficult to helplessly watch one's dreams fade away. Even my dear friend Muna accused me of selfishness and said, "You've been married five years but we have yet to harvest its fruit. Look at me, I'm pregnant with my fourth child!"

My life started to detour into despair and unhappiness. Sometimes I turned into a wild animal that broke things. Then weakness would overcome me. Finally I gave up my stubborn pride and began to consider steps to remedy our problem. I was tired of his mother's harsh words and the accusing looks that followed me everywhere. When Ahmad returned from work, I looked at him with tears in my eyes and said, "I don't want one more day to pass in which you are denied something you want but can't say for fear of hurting me. Even when you know I can read your thoughts, you try to avoid confrontation. I give you the right to act freely. You can marry another to have children. This seems to be the best solution. You're not my prisoner."

"Yes, a second marriage seems unavoidable," he agreed meekly.

Deep inside I screamed. My soul was pulled from its roots and crushed.

Then he left me at his father's house and went to a new job

in Riyadh. My days passed in boredom. Anxiety controlled my thoughts. Time whirled about me like the ghost of loneliness. Miserable, I went to my mother, who was sick in bed. I threw myself in her embrace and wept, but she said matter-of-factly, "As if he were the only man in the world who is being denied parenthood! Reality is a straight bridge. Try to cross it with courage. Get busy, study, find a job."

Suddenly I awoke from the confusion that had kept these answers hidden from me. I started over. I had to struggle even harder, but with courage and determination, I did get busy, and study, and find a job—a teaching position. The work eased my loneliness. My husband didn't even bother to find out what I was up to.

One day when I returned from work, my mother-in-law was waiting for me by her room. She said angrily, "This house has become a hotel for people who don't understand the meaning of respect. You do whatever you like with no man around."

Fed up with always being the weak one and giving in to her, I lashed out, "Of course I do! Where is the man of the house? He's been gone two years now. Go and give *him* a lecture on respect and responsibilities. I have done nothing shameful. I worked to become the master of myself. *Why are you angry with me?* I've stood by you, so don't be hurtful. The harshness of my days hurts me enough. But now you can let me go in peace."

I rushed like a mad woman released from her chains and started packing my clothes. All the blackness of the world gathered in my eyes.

Then I heard his voice, "Where to?"

I looked at him and said, "To my family's house."

But he answered, "Why are you angry? Things were out of my hands. I was transferred."

I said, "I don't care, I'm going home. This isn't a home. I don't like feeling unwanted. You may want to see me now and then, if I happen to intrude upon your dreams. Otherwise, I'm merely a thought for your lips to smile at. You might need me for a moment but then you ask yourself, 'Why do I need her if she can't make me a parent?' You immerse me in guilt. I'm like a person running in a vast desert, who suddenly stops to find the source of a sound in the midst of all those echoes coming from unknown sources. My need for you has taken me to the peak of patience time and again. You've pushed me into a whirlwind of despair, worrying that my role in your life has ended. Even if I've not given you a child, there are rights and obligations in a marriage.² It is important to honor them. But I wanted you to honor them freely. Don't you see how much I want you? Fertility is Allah's gift. If he leaves me otherwise, do I kill myself?"

I gathered myself to leave. But he hugged me and kept repeating, "Please my love, forgive me, and may Allah forgive me."

Notes

1. A child is expected the first year of marriage. Neither the husband nor the wife can be comfortable until children are produced. For the man, a son guarantees the continuation of the house. For the wife, a child proves her fertility and establishes her place in the family and society. Infertility is customarily assumed to be the woman's fault. Even the narrator assumes the problem is hers, not his.

2. He is obliged as her husband to live with her, sleep with her, and support her financially.

The Reflection

Khayriyyah as-Saqqaf

When life is a horror and dreams are not allowed, women often grasp at any new offering. Although marriage may appear to be the best option, a disastrous match can imprison a woman and draw her back into the past from which she tried to escape. Only in her imagination can her wishes come true.

—Editors

All that fills me is the one hope that, if fulfilled, would be an angelic deception falling from shafts of light that would rescue me. When things stand still, I open my eyes to the horror.

I'll find a gallant knight on a gray horse to take me where Sinbad took his love Ira on a wooden horse away from the claws of wild beasts. But I'm still among the beasts, who take away my freedom to make decisions on my own, who control my behavior. They color my smiles and tears. They even weigh the food I eat. It is not shameful, then, that I think of the knight.

"Hey, you!"

Something is speaking to me from somewhere. It might be my subconscious. It could be anything.

"The knight you think about is a myth. This is not the time of horses or knights. Don't you know where the knights went? They died under the horses' feet as they were trying to escape the walls of your people."

I reply to myself, "It doesn't matter. You even want to take away my dreams the moment I enjoy them."

The voice comes again, "Oh you! They're your family, Muna, your father, mother, brothers."

"It doesn't make a difference. There is no difference between them and thieves. Even if they are not actually using the same means, it amounts to the same thing in the end."

I circle my room nervously, fall into the chair in the corner with the dresser and the little desk, and stare at the small rug in the middle of the floor, where some of my papers are scattered. The window is closed, hidden behind a thick curtain. A lonely fly wanders around the room as if seeking escape from the space around it, and finally lands on the top of my nose. I wave my hand at it.

"Oh, you wicked one. Why must you bother me at a moment like this?"

There is unusual movement in the house and then a knock at the door. My brother Khalid enters: "Father is asking: Do you agree to marry him?"

I answer nervously, "*Naim*, yes."

My brother jumps with excitement and quickly leaves the room.

I'm the third out of four. My three brothers are Khalid, Mohammed, and Majed. My father and mother live in a continuous fight. The neighbors often hear their shouts.

I remember the day Mother left the house in fury, with all of us children following her, clinging to the end of her *abayah*. She told us, "Go away, you sons of a dog. I'm leaving. Go to hell, leave me alone."

Hours later, as the sun went down leaving the earth as yellow as the face of a sick person, there was knocking at the door. The curtain was pulled open.

There stood my grandfather and uncle, then the neighbor's children, and behind them, the aunts with their elbows hooked around my mother's. The usual procession, with the silence of funerals. Seconds later my mother's moanings were loud. Father started to shout meaningless words. Everyone left but one of the aunts, who came closer to Mother and commands:

"Don't back down. Wake up! You have to be tough."

The aunt left. She really is a troublemaker. This home has never known peace or quiet.

But Mother had come back to her dog and pups.

* * *

My brothers go and come, I don't know anything about them but their names.[1]

"Ya Khalid, I want a notebook and a pen," I used to ask.

Nobody answered.

"Ya Mohammad, please take me to my girlfriend's house. I would like to visit her."

"Oh really! Girls' nonsense. You have to learn to stay at home, you shouldn't be going out."

"Ya Majed, little brother, please sit down with me, let me talk to you." Silence.

My father has never given me any money. Once I stole some from my classmate's schoolbag. With it I bought this large soccer ball I hide under my bed.

My father is mysterious. All I know of him is his anger and the hand that I kiss mornings and evenings. Otherwise, I would be ironed on both sides by fire, and my day would be hell. Always I feel the sting of fire at the edge of my fingers.

All my father can say is, "Take my clothes and wash them," or shout, "What the hell, whenever I enter your room, I find you reading books." Then he grabs the book from my hand and rips it to shreds, just as he tears my soul and ideas, and orders me, "Go cook and clean. Don't laugh. Wear this and not that. . . ."

* * *

I run out of the house toward my school friends. The young girls care about nothing but the thrill of their flirtations, tricks, and games.

Hifa is spoiled. Her mother listens to her; her father sympathizes with her, and she generally doesn't suffer from abuse.

Ghada is a playgirl. I don't want to see her.

Suad, Fathia, Johara, and others are excellent students. Their parents encourage their studies.

* * *

One day when I left school, I was followed by a voice deep inside, shaking me, "You've got psychological problems . . . problems. . . ."

Another voice was calling me. "Come with us anywhere, let's enjoy our youth, let's laugh and dance and do whatever we like."

A third voice said, "We don't understand you. You're strange. Get involved in your school work and you'll solve all your problems."

"But if you come to my house," I protested, "you will understand what I go through. Actually you've added to my worries, you've broken me, shattered what remains of my self-confidence. You've tried to get me to deviate, or rise to the sky. You didn't succeed in the first or the second. I failed—my circumstances don't help. My family is crowding me. My world is full of greed and evil." That very day I decided to marry, to accept any knight who knocked on my door.

* * *

And then my mother enters and says, "Yellah,[2] Muna. Put on your best clothes."

Why does she speak so softly? I am not used to that from her. She is probably saying to herself, "When she leaves the house, she reduces the expenses. I might even leave her father. The others are boys, I could care for them."

* * *

When I come out to meet my groom I am shocked. He is totally repulsive. Old, with gray hair, his eyes sleeping behind thick glasses—actually his eyes can't be seen through the glasses. His hands are rough, thick, and large.

"Don't worry, Muna," says a voice from inside. "What's important is that you leave this house."

On my first day at the new house I look at him and weep. I heard his hoarse voice asking, "Why are you weeping, my bride?"

I said, "It's nothing."

Why nothing? He doesn't look at all like a knight.

("Didn't I tell you once that this time of ours is not the time of knights on horseback?")

He repeats, "Why are you weeping, Muna?"

"I miss my mother and father." ("You're lying, you didn't succeed in your dreams, that's all.")

He repeats for the third time, "Why are you weeping, oh Muna?"

"Don't you know why I'm weeping?"

"No."

"I'm weeping for my luck."

"It is a happy one, inshallah, with me."

"Inshallah!"

I do not sleep that night. I have moved to an even darker house. There are no birds, no garden, no fragrance of flowers. There is no knight, not even the neighing of a horse. There is no rosy night where voices, laughter, and perfumes are mixed. It is just a dull, dull house.

* * *

How many times have I cried by day and all night? But no one has even seen me. How many times have I searched for someone to understand me, to stand by me? School . . . in school I can find friends and teachers who understand me.

The fat, barefooted old man with the white mustache comes into the room. His face is hidden under his headdress. He looks stern.

"Get up, Muna, prepare some food. I've guests with me."

"Yes, sir."

I move slowly looking under the bed for my shoes. I bend to pick one up, but fall down.

Kicking me, the old man shouts, "I said now!"

I raise my face toward him and yell: "Stop! Enough! Why are you beating me?"

The old man beats me and shouts, "I am divorcing you!"

I carry my daughter and my *abayah* with me. I don't find anything else worth taking. I no longer care about anything. I just need fresh air. I rush to the street, with rivers of tears streaming down my face.

* * *

My new "father" is a mere reflection of my old one, except

that he beats me even more, insults me more, and he's even older. One day I pull out my wedding dress and throw it from the window into the garbage lot. I gather my hair and cover it, and break all my perfume bottles. I don't leave any of my make-up on my dresser, throwing it away.

I continue in the journey of pain and bad luck. The long street is swallowing me. I am lost in my tears.

I hear a hoarse voice far behind. I hear, "Muna, stop!" in the midst of the crowd. . . .

I'm dizzy, have a headache, vomit, and collapse on the street. I disappear under the feet. . . .

Notes

1. Segregation by gender begins at an early age. Therefore it is common for a young girl to have separate social activities from those of her brothers.

2. "Come on."

PART THREE

*Love:
Romantic, Requited,
and Otherwise*

I Will Not Return

Qumashah al-ᶜUlayyan

Even in a nation that prescribes the death penalty for adultery, this philanderer's wife assumes for a very long time the traditional need for a woman to accept her fate. Why does she take so long to rebel?

—Editors

Mariam knew Ibrahim was cheating on her but kept quiet. He knew that she knew, and went to extremes. They had married after a long and wonderful love story all on one side—hers. She had loved him since the first moment her eyes looked upon the world. He was her cousin, a handsome young man. She wasn't alone in her love for him. All the young girls in her family and outside loved him. He'd been the dream of every girl, the hope of every spinster, and the wish of every girl's mother. In addition to being handsome, he thrived on success—in school, in managing his father's business, in his social relations. Mariam loved him. She never tried to draw his attention to herself, not even to show a small portion of what was in her longing heart. Her friends used to insist she phone him, but she had refused and kept her love to herself. Some girls had telephoned him, others had sent him letters, still others had sent him music cassettes, and some had even gone out with him.[1] Too many for her to have any hope, especially since she had refused to parade her love as the others did. She knew she wasn't as pretty as most of the others. She also wasn't educated beyond high school, and had no career. But to her surprise, and to the surprise of all, he had asked for her hand in marriage—her's and not any other girl's.

* * *

She was tongue-tied. Her mother asked her for the second time:

"Mariam, you haven't answered. Do you agree to marry Ibrahim?"

Words came out with difficulty and she said, "It's up to you. . . . I just don't know."

Her mother smiled widely. She interpreted her daughter's confusion as the shyness of every young woman.

Mariam closed her doors and looked at everything as if for the first time: the doors, windows, her bed, her pillow, her clothes. Everything looked different, everything was magically changed. Life was gaiety and happiness. But no, she couldn't be happy until she knew why he chose her from the rest of the girls. There had to be a reason.

But then her joy made her forget everything. It was enough that he chose her. On her wedding day, happiness glittered in her eyes when she saw him. But she also overheard nasty comments and sarcastic laughs that hurt her. One said, "She doesn't suit him at all. She's not even pretty."

She also overheard a mother scold her daughter saying, "Do you see her intelligence? She isn't beautiful, but she won everything."

Mariam held her head proudly, and left holding the arm of her handsome groom.

That night she asked him, "Why did you choose me, when there were so many others?"

He was silent for a moment. Then said, "Perhaps you're the only one that I couldn't get. The only one who didn't try to throw her net around me. The only one of whom I didn't see even her finger, until our wedding night."

Days passed as she tried to learn all his emotions and feelings. She tried to reach his heart, to become everything in his life despite her simplicity.

But soon he returned to his old habits. Girls swarmed around him everywhere he went. Many even became daring, perhaps to displease his wife.

She kept silent, but people around her were talking; they whispered about her husband's sexual adventures. The whispers grew louder, began to shout in her face: "Your husband is cheating on you."

Her silence became even tighter. Still, she didn't fail him as a wife. She tried even harder to make him love her and his home.

Her mother whispered to her one day that children tie a man to his home. She had their first baby boy, and a second, and then a baby girl. But nothing tied him to her. He traveled abroad and returned carrying photos taken with girls. Her heart sank as she examined these, but she was paralyzed. She couldn't leave him.

On one of her desperate days an old friend visited her and said, "Don't you have any feelings? Your husband is acting like a teenager. Can you imagine, he is flirting with my daughter Rana?"

Mariam was shocked. Though she knew her husband's ways, she couldn't believe it. Rana was only fifteen.

She opened her mouth to talk, but her friend snapped, "You're a fool. But tell him to leave my daughter alone, otherwise we'll have to handle the situation ourselves."

Her friend left, slamming the door behind her.

Mariam remained motionless, an orphan question on her lips. Her home was about to fall apart, her life about to crumble. She had to try something.

So she went to the hairdresser and came out with a new look. She bought the most beautiful dress she saw. Then she went to her sister Ayman, who was well known for her make-up artistry. That evening, she sat in front of the television and waited for her husband. She heard the key turning in the door. She improved her pose a little and smiled for him. He didn't even look at her, but went upstairs to bed.

She followed, her hope fading as despair invaded her heart. She stood in front of him fully adorned, with her heart beating fast. He looked at her and said carelessly,

"Mariam, what do you want? I'm very tired and want to sleep."

"I want nothing," she said hoarsely.

She left the room, drawing her failure behind her, hot tears falling from her eyes. She wept for her lost life, her lost love. Regret pushed away what remained of her love for him. Why had she agreed to marry him? Why did she keep allowing him to defeat her? Why didn't she drive him out of her life? She was *not* less than he.

In the morning she went to her family's home, bringing her sadness and pain. No one asked her why she'd come. They all knew. They had expected her sooner.

She tried to control her longing for her children by being very tough on herself. She stifled her heart, her love, and feelings. He didn't deserve her.

Her children phoned daily to tell her how sad their father was and to beg her to return. She wouldn't. He had despised, humiliated, and degraded her, making her a joke people told in their spare time. He didn't deserve anything at all from her. He was too arrogant to call her, but brought his mother to take care of the children in her absence.

Boldly she asked her family to request a divorce.[2] In the beginning he hesitated and tried to delay, but finally consented.

When she received the divorce document, announcing the end of her love on the rock of reality, she wept. No, she didn't regret asking for the divorce. But she regretted having wasted years of her life pursuing unfruitful love, and she longed for her children.

* * *

Another man asked for her hand in marriage. He was not as handsome as her ex-husband, nor as successful. He was a teacher with a failed marriage and a six-year-old daughter. He was tender and open-minded. Because he too had suffered in his last marriage, he deeply respected and longed for an ideal married life.

She found herself in agreement with him. They shared the same interests, hobbies, and sincerity. She had finally found what she was looking for. She agreed to marry him and was very sure she would be happy with him. They would not fail.

When Ibrahim heard about her engagement, his conceit fought with his pride. He ran to her, with the three children. She hugged her children and wept a little, but received him very coldly. He beseeched her, "Mariam, will you not return? The children and I need you."

Quietly and firmly Mariam said, "I'm sorry, I won't return. There is another man in my life."

Notes

1. Western-style dating is not common in the Kingdom of Saudi Arabia and is even considered somewhat scandalous.
2. A woman's family must approach the husband and ask him to grant her a divorce. According to Islamic law, she cannot divorce her husband directly but can request a divorce under certain circumstances.

If Only It Were Pity

Lamia Baeshen

Is love more or less important to an Arab woman than an economically sound marriage contract? Though the narrator respects and pities her husband, she resents her poverty. Later, after having truly loved him, she bitterly disagrees with the Western concept that " 'Tis better to have loved and lost/ Than never to have loved at all."
—Editors

It is a night like any other night; I lie on the bed next to him after I pull down the mosquito net. I look at his face in the dense darkness and examine his features carefully. He is sleeping soundly, and I feel a surge of tenderness flow inside me as I watch his chest rise and fall regularly. Each breath he takes confirms his deep-rooted love for me.

Only I know how much he loves me, only I know my place in his heart, and his intense adoration for me. Why, then, am I incapable of returning his passion? More than once have I blamed my cold heart for not being touched by him. I fail to find a single fault in him. Many women would be eager to marry a man with his intellect. Like everyone who knows him, I admire the genius of this outstanding school teacher. His looks? Few men are as handsome as this well-built thirty-year-old man. What is missing, then, for me to respond to my poor husband? It's strange how I could cause the pain that shows on his sleeping face! I do my best to appear loving and kind, but his pure heart can surely tell between feigned and true love. I only wish. . . . I touch his forehead with my lips and sincerely wish him a good night and us a fresh tomorrow.

Suddenly his piercing screams shake me out of my sleep. I

don't know if I have slept minutes or hours, but I am frightened by his hand clutching my arm and his desperate voice groaning, "Help!" I try to calm him, until his increasing pain makes me panic and turn to my husband's kin for help.

Yes! It is the same night, but it has not been like any other night. A night my husband has spent with the doctors in our bedroom, and I have spent breathless and shaking outside with his family. A night at the end of which he is transferred to the hospital, to come back to me after a month of medical rescue procedures, half a man! A stroke has left my poor husband's left side paralyzed. I see in his eyes the real pain of his tragedy: his rejection of my tears, his hatred of the adversity that finally aroused emotion in my heart. It is an emotion he refuses to accept, because it patronizes his manhood, his talents, his intelligence, and his charm. He doesn't want my pity.

But with pity we have lived ever since. His sad shadow moves silently around the small house and I, in my fresh youth, follow him from room to room, contemplating our misfortune. On his desk are piles of books he does not open, pens and brushes he does not touch, records he does not listen to. In my arms is the two-year-old daughter he does not dandle anymore; in his eyes, a sparkling tear struggling not to fall; and in my heart, only pity.

One morning, my husband leans on his cane and leaves the house to resume his work. In his absence I gaze upon the small house that was furnished by my father on my wedding day. Not one piece has been added to it. Here are the same clothes that my family stocked in my closet; I have not been able to purchase even a new scarf. And there is the knocking on the door: it's the boy servant bringing a tray of food from my husband's family—food my husband cannot, with his meager salary, provide us. Maybe my indifference toward him has been the result of his inability to clothe me in silk, ornament my neck with pearls, and fill my table with gourmet food. Perhaps I have not been able to love him because I could never compete with my sisters and my relatives by showing off a new piece of furniture or a new dress.

But what kind of love is regulated only by material pursuits?[1] How can I overlook all the other things he has given me? How can I ignore the value my mind has gained from our conversations? Has he not taught me that my hands are to be used for more important things than housework? How can I forget the hours he spent teaching me the alphabet, letter by letter, until I mastered reading and writing, though I could never match his craft of penmanship? How can I deny him credit for explaining the subtle meanings of poetry and literature to me? Even the songs I used to repeat like a parrot in my tender years have acquired new significance thanks to him. Patiently and lovingly he introduced to my simple understanding all the wonderful poems sung by Mohammad Abdul Wahab: al-Karnak, Cleopatra, and al-Gondol.

> *Every heart has beaten, every tongue has chanted*
> *She is this life's wonder*
> *She is all-times' marvel*
> *O my darling, this is the night of my love*
> *Will you come and share the joys of my heart?*

A knock on the door interrupts my thoughts. It is my aunt. After I welcome her, we sit down to chat while my little girl sleeps in my lap. As she inquires about my husband's health, I see pity for me in her eyes. She goes further, expressing sadness for my calamity, and suddenly throws in a strange suggestion: she thinks it is best that I leave my home! That kind of sympathy amazes me. With utter callousness she proceeds, "The man is no good now. He is only half a man." I truly wish she would quit, but she pushes her venom further by saying that paralysis is contagious and that I may get it if I remain near my husband too long. I finally ask her to stop. Her hurtful words prompt me to assert that I have no intention of leaving my husband in his time of need. But she dives into my obstinacy, comes closer, and asks me in a whisper to promise solemnly not to let this man touch me, for paralysis is hereditary too. Flabbergasted, my tears answer her strange request. She thinks she sees my submission to her desire and leaves in peace.

This evening, with all the love he insultingly calls pity, and with all the hope of changing our life together into paradise, I long for my husband to come home. I listen to his shaking cane climbing up the wooden staircase slowly and carefully. I rush to open the door and receive him at the doorstep. I offer a hand; he hesitates but takes it. I lead him to his office, open for him his neglected books, and dip in ink his deserted brushes. Then

I watch his dear hand at work drawing lines as graceful as the enchanting music of al-Karnak, which fills the room and directs his perplexed eyes to my face in search of an answer: Is it love or pity this time?

Nine months later, a beautiful face looks up to us: our son Ghali, the seed of the love in my heart, flowering in the image of his compassionate, tender-hearted father. Does my husband want greater confirmation of my love for him? There is no explanation for this strange likeness except one: this child has grown inside my heart. A child as intelligent as his father, a child my aunt has warned will carry his disability!

I swear I have known no such happiness before the birth of our son. My husband and I spend our years in bliss: he carries out his daily routine with a bright face and a radiant soul, as I see him off with one smile and receive him with another. Around us Ghali and his sister Lulu grow up to fill our life with pleasure.

Until one night like any other night, I lie next to him after pulling down the mosquito net. When I examine his features in the dense darkness, I find him still awake looking at me with eyes full of undying love. He whispers: Shukran, thank you. I smile, resting my head on his shoulder and ready to submit to the power of sleep. Then the silence of night is torn again by his shrill screams. I wake up frightened by his hand clenching my arm as he calls for help. I embrace his weary head, trying to calm him in vain. His increasing pain pushes me out of bed, looking for the boy servant to send to his family. In the pitch darkness of the night they take him to the hospital. But a few days later they bring back his corpse.

My husband, Abu Ghali, has died. He has left me a widow in my twenties, with a gaping wound in my heart. I wish I'd never tried to love him. I wish I'd remained pitying and sympathetic only. I wish my heart had remained hard and frigid so that it couldn't have been broken.

As I depart from the small home that housed our grand love, I leave behind all the furniture my father brought on my wedding day, and all the clothes my family stocked in my closet, to be sold in the market for a very small price. I walk back to my family's house,[2] followed by two children who carry his name. I bring with me only sketches drafted by his graceful fingers, brushes touched by his hands, books embraced by his eyes, and records we heard and sang together:

O my darling, this is the night of my love
Will you come and share the joys of my heart?

Notes

1. Traditionally women have viewed marriage as a relationship of set responsibilities and duties. Love may or may not occur. Young women and men, however, are now questioning this attitude and expectations have started to change, with the younger generation looking more for romantic love in marriage.

2. After divorce or the death of a spouse, a woman returns to her father's house. Women do not usually live alone, outside the umbrella of family members, in Saudi society.

Fall Nights

Samirah Khashuqji

This story examines both Bara'ah's objection to polygyny (though most Westerners would object for reasons other than hers) and her persistent submission to a boring marriage. Is it material wealth she desires or a modern relationship?

—*Editors*

As she closed the door to leave, Bara'ah sighed in contentment. Every Friday[1] her husband allowed her to go to the club where she relaxed completely for a whole day. On that day, she spent time with her friends and enjoyed a few hours like a lady who is not concerned with housework, taking care of her children, or listening to her husband's problems. What a monotonous and boring life she led, and what tedious stories her husband told her! To give her a break, her husband, Salim, allowed her to be free for a day and didn't even return home for lunch, but ate out with one of his friends.

What had happened to Salim? He used to be so gentle and amusing! When had he become so talkative, tedious, and irritating? She felt that she, too, had changed for the worse. She had become mechanical, moving about the house nervously and doing housework mindlessly. When she sat with her husband to watch TV in the evening, she felt tired and sometimes gave in to sleep, not waking until Salim said jokingly: "My wife is epileptic with sleep sickness. She can even sleep sitting up." Bara'ah would wake up hearing him talk but couldn't always tell whether this was real or a dream. Then she'd go to bed.

Days passed in this manner. But was this the life she once desired?

* * *

Once while she was in the club waiting for her friend Huyam, Bara'ah's mind wandered and she remembered a time when she was sixteen and her dream prince was twenty-five, strong, and tall. The sun had seared him and his body looked as if it were made of copper. His eyes were sharp and his lips curved.

She met him at a party where her uncle introduced him saying, "This is Emir Zahid, and this is my niece Bara'ah." She gazed at him in amazement. This was her first encounter with a real prince. She gave him a little shy smile and asked, "Are you really a prince?" Prince Zahid smiled and answered: "Yes, but I don't care for titles." She smiled joyfully and said, "Then you're the dream prince." The next day, her uncle invited Zahid to his home and asked Bara'ah to come for dinner.

She went to the beauty salon and after an hour came out feeling proud and confident. She felt overwhelmingly beautiful with her hair done and her new dress. She looked like a princess. Her heart was beating. She felt shy, puzzled, and hesitant.

She went to her uncle's house and met the prince. He extended his hands and held her hand in both of his, saying, "I am glad to see you."

He then looked at her attentively from head to foot. She could tell that she attracted him. Pleasure consumed her when he said, "You are so beautiful and elegant. And you blush like a little girl." Bara'ah hesitated and said, "Thank you for your kindness."

She again raised her brown eyes. Surprisingly, she witnessed an attractive brightness in his eyes that shone whenever he was happy. He eagerly asked her, "Are you finished with school?"

"I just received my high school diploma and plan to enroll at the university next year."

Her uncle was happy. He was sure that the prince liked Bara'ah. He might even ask to marry her.

That, in fact, happened the next day. Prince Zahid made the proposal to her uncle. Her family held a quick meeting in which her father approved the marriage.

Bara'ah was ecstatic. The prince offered her precious gifts.

The newspapers even wrote of their love story and her expected marriage to the prince.

Soon after, her uncle came calmly to her and said, "I have to be frank with you, Bara'ah. Prince Zahid is, in fact, already married to his cousin and has five children. But that doesn't matter.[2] Our religion allows a man to marry up to four women, and he'll make you happy with his love and wealth. You'll have prosperity, prestige, and happiness."

Bara'ah kept her silence for a moment, as she looked at her uncle in astonishment and confusion. Then she shouted, "I'll never marry a married man, even if he offers me all the treasures of the world!"

She turned to leave, but her uncle held her: "Be rational, Bara'ah. You'll regret it. He's the best groom you'll ever find."

At that moment, she despised her uncle. She looked at him in pain and said, "You, and my father, and all the family are not concerned about the man. Your concern is money. I want a man who will belong to me. Let the prince and his money go away. I am not a bonded woman to be sold. I am a free woman with dignity and pride!"

Bara'ah sought a happy married life of love and tenderness. How could she be happy at the expense of another woman's misery? After this, she was ill-disposed. She had terrifying nightmares that shook her and often woke her with a cry trapped in her throat.

At the university, she met Salim. She admired his kindness, good manners, and calmness, and even began to feel more cheerful. Throughout the university years, their relationship didn't go beyond mere friendship, but when she graduated, he asked to see her and said softly, "Oh Bara'ah, I really can't live without you. I would like to marry you." Bara'ah smiled calmly and confessed, "It would please me to marry you, Salim." His face blazed with pleasure. He hugged her and said happily, "Right now I will ask your father for your hand." And they were married.

* * *

The years passed quickly until life became routine. Bara'ah began to question herself. Why was her life so boring? Would she have been better off with the prince? But the answer was negative.

She could find no answers. One day when she saw her friend Huyam they began to talk.

"What's wrong, Bara'ah? You look pale."

"Nothing. I'm all right."

"Did you have a fight with Salim?"

"No."

"Then you must be bored. Didn't I tell you before graduation that married life dulls over the years?"

"There's no need to say such a thing. Salim is good-hearted, but he's always busy."

"But you, what's wrong? Don't you have the right to enjoy the time you spend with him? Don't you have the right to spend time with him? Be frank and tell him what's on your mind. Why hide your feelings? Don't let boredom eat away at you. You do love him, Bara'ah. Don't let the happiness of your household slip away from you, don't turn your children away and become like a breaking rock, swallowed by the sea. Believe me, if he feels something for you, he'll change."

Coincidentally, Salim was late that night. When he returned home, Bara'ah met him with eyes full of tears. She told him in a weepy voice, "What a boring life! I can't stand the house and the children because of your attitude." Salim was taken aback. He calmly said, "There's no need for such turmoil, darling. Why do I work hard and get tired? Don't you know? All this is for you and the children."

Bara'ah insisted, "Stop it, Salim. Other husbands work hard for their families, too! But some husbands know that their wives have the right to enjoy life."

She paused for a moment and continued in a hoarse voice, "Life is not just food, clothes, and money. You're wrong if you think that."

Salim embraced her, full of passion and love. Their eyes met: "Give me another chance to make you happy. You're my life, my hope, my ambitions," he pleaded.

Bara'ah put her head on his shoulder. How pleased she was to put her tired head on his kind chest.

Whenever she remembered her friend Huyam, her eyes filled with tears of gratitude.

Notes

1. Thursday and Friday comprise the Saudi weekend. Friday is the Muslim day of worship and rest.

2. Polygyny is allowed according to Islamic tradition. A man may have up to four wives at the same time, but only on condition that he is able to treat them equally and provide each a separate place of residence. Polygyny is most commonly found among the wealthy or the elite. But presently the practice is in decline, as more young women refuse to marry into a family as the second, third, or fourth wife.

A Single-Winged Bird

Lamia Baeshen

This story centers around the daughter of a culturally mixed marriage. When she falls in love, questions of identity arise: "Is she Mariam, a Saudi Arabian girl, or Mary, a blonde American girl?" Whom does her suitor truly love?
—Editors

I leapt up suddenly and hastened away as fast as I could. When I closed my eyes my feet rushed away from him even faster. From him—the dream of my life, the only person who I ever thought could understand my true self. "Mariam!" he called behind me. "What is the matter? Mariam!"

I blocked my ears, which had always been so eager to hear his voice calling my name.

Only a few minutes before, I had floated in the sky of ecstasy. The moment I had lived for had finally come. He was sitting next to me, saying, "Mariam, I am very much attracted to you. If you have no objection, I will ask my uncle for your hand in marriage."

My heart flying toward him, I whispered, "Attracted to me?"

"Who else, Mariam? Don't tell me you've never noticed. You and I loved each other when we were only children, although we never confessed our love. Where is the surprise?"

"I thought I had only imagined our love," I said in a low voice, "Especially after your travels, which took you away and filled your life with so many options. I used to ask myself what advantage I could have over all the others, for you to single me out?"

"Silly!" he grinned. "Where else would I find a woman as

beautiful as you? I have always been charmed by your blue eyes and soft golden hair and your lovely fair skin."

His words echoed in my ears like thunder and I jumped to my feet in disappointment. A voice was roaring in my ears, "Which one of us does he really want? Me or Mary?" A whirling mass of anger engulfed me and swept me from him, from the garden, from the world.

His hateful voice hunted me: "Mariam, wait a minute! What is the matter?" But I had no wish to answer.

My feet ran up the stairs that led to the main door—the same door where, as a seven-year-old, I had waited for it to open, my heart full of terror. "Go in, Mariam!" I had been told. The two strangers, the man and the woman, were extending their arms to receive me. "This is your family now, Mariam. You will live happily with them."

Unwillingly, I had dragged my feet into the big house, looking back to see Granny's silhouette at the door becoming smaller and smaller until it disappeared, like any other figure disappearing on any delivery day.

"Which one of us does he really want? Mary or me?"

Running the long hallway through the mist of tears I saw more shadows of memory. My family was in that same living room as I passed. Ahmed and Iman and I were playing, and Iman asked Mother, "Why is Mariam's hair yellow?"

I raised my eyes to read Mother's lips as she answered softly, "It is Allah's own doing." I breathed again.

But then Ahmed remarked, "If Mariam is really our sister, then Mother must have been wishing awfully hard for a Barbie doll when she was pregnant." I stared at Mother's mouth, waiting for a convincing answer, but she had no comment, and again I felt I was suffocating.

Iman poked her silence: "Is it true, Mother? Did you wish for a Barbie when you were pregnant?"

"This is ridiculous!" she answered abruptly. "As I said before, it was Allah's own doing." She looked nervous.

"Then why does Mariam look more like Barbie than like us?" Ahmed's question burst forth. Yes, I wondered too. But Mother had no answer for us. In an unexplained fury she drove us out of the room. That same day, the Barbie doll disappeared from our toy box.

Incidents like this recurred constantly, in schools and social calls, everywhere. They always ended in chilly somberness and questions without answers; in the family, the subject was forbidden. Why was I different? Why did I look like no one but that hateful Barbie?

When I was ten I could bear it no longer. Once when she visited us, I faced Granny in the garden and demanded, "Tell me, Granny, where did you bring me from?"

She stared at me over the glasses that rested on the tip of her nose and stammered, "What an absurd thing to ask, Mariam!"

"But I heard Mother talking on the phone today. She was saying, 'Oh, it hurts to look at her, because she always reminds me of the other woman.'"

"But why do you think she was talking about you?"

"Please, Granny, this is not the first time." I had previously gathered fragments of an important secret that concerned me—gathered both accidentally, through someone's slip of the tongue, and intentionally, through close eavesdropping and observing. "Do I have another mother? A different mother than Iman's and Ahmed's? Different from Mother?"

That day, Granny had no choice but to whisper the truth to me. The devastating truth. Poor Granny had to reveal it as tenderly as she could, and then she had to bear my raging anger for keeping it from me for so long. When I began to scream and wail, she held me in her arms to ease my pain.

After that I retreated into the shade. Only my cousin could invade my solitary world, I thought. His eyes could penetrate my walls, and his ears could hear my suppressed cries. Were my thoughts so erroneous, then? After all the time that I had waited for him, he was choosing Mary instead of me!

On the way to my room I glimpsed Iman, glued as usual to the telephone.

The telephone. The idea had crossed my mind before: "Hello. Seattle, Washington? I would like to talk to . . ."

But I didn't even know her name or address.

"Granny," I once asked anxiously, "can I call her on the phone?"

"No!" she answered, hitting the dough in the bottom of the tray as if she were slapping my face.

"Can I write a letter?" I implored.

"No!" said the dough-hitter resolutely. "You will make me

regret telling you the truth, Mariam. You and I promised on that day that we would never again bring up this subject."

My father's strict orders had dictated that I should never know my mother, so I grew up knowing nothing about her, and feeling orphaned. When I was very small, I thought for awhile that Granny was my mother, because I lived with her and she took care of me so tenderly after our visit to the doctor's office:

"This stuttering is a natural reaction to her early separation from her first home."

Granny lavished so much love upon me that she straightened out my tongue. But when I was seven I heard her say, "Out of sight, out of mind. My son will forget her if she stays with me any longer. She is his daughter, a member of his family, and she has to grow up in his care." That was when she took me to live with Mother and Father and Iman and Ahmed.

After I learned that I had another mother—the *khawaja*—the Westerner—I pretended not to be bothered by it, but a thousand voices urged me to search for her. Why did she leave me, or why were we separated, when I was just four years old? Why couldn't I remember her? But the unconscious mind must have power, for after Granny's confession I started to remember a blonde lady whose heart was full of tender love. Although I feigned indifference in front of the others, each night before I went to sleep, my suppressed cries pressed my memory for the mysterious woman with the soft blue eyes and bright golden hair parted on the right side, the woman who would never again look upon me with her beautiful round face, the woman who gave me life and then disappeared forever. Away from watching guards, Mama and I whispered discreetly to each other every night. She called me "Mary."

My crying and running left me breathless as the questions crashed against my skull, the questions that arose whenever I sat by myself to avoid the curious stares of strangers. "Who am I? One foot is here, but the other doesn't even know where *there* is. What kind of woman is my mother, really? Did she love Father? Did she love me? How could Father forget her and make me forget her too? Why did he hate her so much that he canceled her from his life and mine?" In order to part with my past to plan a future, I first had to find my lost past, or I'd keep on flying in aimless circles, directionless.

Her bedroom door was ajar and she was combing her hair,

that woman who had intruded into my father's and my life. Our enemy, surely; did she not occupy my mother's place in his heart? She must have had something to do with my father's renunciation of my mother. Yet she had always been nice to me, so I had never faced her with any antagonism. But Mary was always suspicious of her. Sometimes Mary flared up at her and defied her openly, a behavior I found very embarrassing.

My dispute with Mary intensified, until it had almost cut me in half.

Why had Mary won *his* love? How had I lost it?

"You are a rare bride, Mariam," he had repeated so foolishly. "Any man would dream of marrying you. Where else could he find such a fantastic combination? An Arab in a beautiful European form?"

Enough! My appearance was a trap that imprisoned me in suspicion and curiosity. I was a circus freak who attracted onlookers, a creature without history, a stranger among strangers. Oh, how I wished I could disappear amid the crowds!

Impatiently I turned my doorknob. As usual, I felt safe when I found her sitting there with her round face smiling affectionately, her blue eyes calm and loving. She signaled me to come closer and whispered, "Mary, darling!"

"Hello, Mama!"

Wishing to cry into her golden hair, I poured out my heart to her. She rose and spread her arms to embrace me. I dashed toward her, and she hurried toward me. I drew closer to her and she drew closer to me. Just as I almost touched her, we both smashed into the cold, sleek, and shiny mirror.

The Last Dream

Mona A. Al-Dokair

If a woman cannot tell her family that she is in love because she cannot hope to marry the man, then dreaming is perhaps her only option—especially if her traditional society bans marriage to a stranger or any other kind of foreigner. Then her only possible dream is that he will dare come to her rescue.

—Editors

Sabeeka lay on the light cotton bed suffering from fever and a bad headache. Whenever she gained consciousness, she couldn't stop crying and asking for Allah's pardon. "Ya Allah, forgive me, protect my secrets, and let my death be virtuous."

Her mother sat with her. She wore an old dress with an embroidered black *thobe* over it, but nothing of the golden embroidery remained worth its name. It was a long *thobe* whose hem trailed behind her as she went into the dusty kitchen. She pulled it up to her midriff and tied it carefully. The smell of cooking spread from her as she leaned close to her daughter lying before her.

"La illah illa Allah![1] There is no god but Allah! The evil eye has caught you, an eye that does not pray on the Prophet. Ya Sabeeka, oh, my little mama, do you hear me?"

She placed her hand on Sabeeka's forehead. Sabeeka opened her faint dark eyes with tears on her lashes, "Mother, I'm dying. please forgive me for everything."

"Don't worry about anything you have done in your life, poor one. Allah will forgive you and us."

* * *

Maher was the love that ran through her soul. He was like the night breeze on the roof of their house on hot summer nights. Now her gaze wandered outside where she used to meet her love.

Her younger sister sat near her head, braiding Sabeeka's long black hair. Her eyes shone with the surprise of someone who doesn't know what was happening around her. Why was this surrendering apparent in her mother, this sadness binding her father? She wiped the sweat from Sabeeka's forehead. How many times had she and Sabeeka raced, climbing the stone steps, spreading cotton mattresses on the rooftop in the afternoon, putting out pillows for all the family?

After sunset, Sabeeka would go down the stairs alone in the dark. She was a little afraid, but not afraid to go and see Maher. She would cross the narrow alley that separated their homes.

"What is the matter with my sister, Mother? She seemed fine until now. Let's take her to the clinic."

"No, there is no need. I brought her some herbs from the herbalist. I'll boil some for her to drink. She'll be all right, inshallah."

Sabeeka's skinny old father had been beaten by years of pearl diving in those dark seas. He had suffered from poverty and from missing his wife when he used to leave for six months at a time. Then he would come back and behave as if he hadn't been absent a day and so he was treated by her mother. His sarong showed under his yellowish *dishdasha* as he sat by Sabeeka's side. How many times had Sabeeka's brother Musaed tried to convince Father to put on slippers like the old men of the neighborhood, but he insisted on going barefoot.

Sabeeka sighed.

"My daughter, may the name of Allah protect you. My little Sabeeka, how do you feel?" her father worried.

"I have a headache, my father. My head is about to explode."

Her father murmured, "It is enough to have Allah. He is the trusted one." He rubbed her forehead with his rough hand while reciting verses from the Quran. Then he stood up and left the room.

Where was Musaed? She hadn't seen him but once, when

he had stood silently over her head. For a moment, she had felt a look of malice in his eyes, and had shivered. Now she was drowning in fever.

Musaed was the only son. Their father had scolded their mother to stop spoiling him. He had left school early and started to spend time in the streets, flirting with the girls in the neighborhood and coming back late at night with a strange smell in his mouth. His mother hit him once when the girls asked her why she scolded him.

Little Dalal, her maternal cousin, sat by her side feeding her a hot meat soup. "By Allah, Sabeeka, there is nothing wrong with you. You're just spoiled."

Sabeeka smiled at the teasing. Dalal was her friend and the keeper of her secrets. She had told Sabeeka many stories about her school friends after Sabeeka was taken out of school very young when her mother noticed that her beauty drew too much attention.[2] The neighboring women had started to allude to their desire that Sabeeka be the future wife for one of their sons.

Musaed suddenly entered the room, looked at his cousin Dalal, and called her. She jumped toward him, and he talked as if he were ordering her, as if he were in control of her. She repeated, "Yes . . . yes." When he left, Sabeeka called with a faint voice, "Dalal."

"Yes, Sabeeka."

"Dalal, I'm dying. I feel it. Do you remember Maher's letters? Take them and tear them into pieces. They are in the wooden chest under my clothes. I don't want to leave behind a black memory. I don't want my mother not to bless me when she remembers me. Go quickly and do as I ask you."

* * *

Sabeeka recalled the first day she saw Maher as she was standing behind the crack in the door, watching passersby to get rid of her boredom. Her mother was gone to distribute the bread and sweets to the neighbors for the small sums that would contribute to the family budget. At this hour her father would be at the cafe sitting with his old friends, and her sister would have gone to school with the neighbor's daughter.

They took her out of school very early to get her married,

but her heart was stolen when her eyes fell on their neighbor, Maher. He was fair as she had never seen before, tall and handsome, with golden hair and a mustache.

She loved him with all her heart. She used to wait for him to return from work each day at the same time. He quickly noticed her. He would slow down for a moment before he entered his home and send her a dizzying smile.

Days passed and she continued to admire his striking looks, which differed from the surrounding tired faces. His eyes were different from the faded black eyes. Oh, they were different! They were clear and beautiful. She could not decide exactly what their true color was. She was satisfied by the distant look that made her heart shiver like a lost bird on its way back to its nest.

Sabeeka turned in her bed as she thought about the tender memories that lightened her heart. One day Maher came courageously close to their door. She rewarded him with such a dazzling smile, he almost fell.

She could not keep her secret to herself, so she told everything to Dalal. Joyously, she felt that she was moving on to a new life. Lights shone in the distance, promising new delights. Her hopes filled her with vague anticipation. Those hours were among her happiest.

* * *

Dalal's lovely laughter came before her. She kissed her aunt and sat by Sabeeka. Sabeeka was in the courtyard slowly combing her long hair, which fell around her like a magical black cascade. She combed it while her gaze was wandering after a great dream. The radio which sat on a wooden shelf was playing a love song:

Stand and dance for me,
Take off the cloak
Let me enjoy my thirst for seeing you.

Dalal whispered, "Let's go to your room." She followed, braiding her hair. Her heart felt that Dalal was carrying good news. Dalal handed her a folded letter she was hiding in her blouse. Sabeeka laughingly snatched it. Breathing quickly, she held it firmly in both hands.

Then she kissed the letter, unfolded it, and read. Maher had dedicated an "epic" of love to her that day. She twirled in circles, her pony tail wrapped around her neck.

"Do you hear? I am his love," she said.

For some moments a pale envious smile was drawn on Dalal's face. Why couldn't she find someone to write her love letters? But she quickly dismissed the thought, for she truly loved Sabeeka.

Dalal became their letter carrier. One day, Maher asked her, "Why did Sabeeka quit school so early?"

"Because she is very beautiful, and my aunt was afraid of obtrusive looks. She is preparing her to marry a rich man."

Maher was shocked. He never thought of such a possibility. Sabeeka had seemed to him a dream or a beautiful mirage. He wrote her asking her to marry him, asking her if there was hope. He had heard from friends that the girls here did not marry strangers. What should he do?

Sabeeka wept. She knew that there was no hope. Yet she really loved him and he was her choice. Her heart could not accommodate anyone else. Life without him was meaningless.

Sabeeka suffered and stopped eating as a kind of unannounced protest. Her mother noticed her thinness. She smiled and said, "Don't worry. Soon you will marry. Umm Salah will come to ask your hand for her son. They are rich and own a *hajj* company."[3]

Silently Sabeeka shouted, "I don't want to get married now!"

Instead she said, "Mother, can you imagine, Dalal said there is a girl at her school from a good family who married a young man not from this area."[4]

"What! I seek Allah's protection from Satan. The Day of Resurrection has come. Where is the family of this lioness?" shouted her mother so loudly that Sabeeka was silently defeated.

* * *

She screamed in unbearable pain. "Mother, help me mother! I'm dying!"

Her mother rushed to her side, "Ya binti! Oh my daughter!"

She embraced Sabeeka passionately as if she were afraid that she would escape. Tears poured down her face.

Her father came running, tripping on the end of his sarong, looking at her face. For the first time he feared death, which was attacking one of his most beautiful children. When he was in the diving *dhow*[5] and one of his comrades died, he had rushed to clean the corpse, wrap it in a white sheet, and drop it into the water. But now he held fast to his daughter, Sabeeka. He would not let her drown like the others. His hands held her shoulders as if he were trying to pick her out of the deep sea. "Ya binti, my daughter," he repeated. His tears fell on her hot forehead.

She let out a faint, fearful cry. He remembered one day when the rope that was always tied around the diver's waist became tangled around his neck, shoulders, and arms, like a black octopus squeezing him. He removed the clip from his nose. He swallowed water, he was suffocating. He swam hard upward, and finally reached the light and the air. They laid him flat on the floor of the *dhow* with many hands touching him. He took a strong breath that brought him back to life.

Musaed stood tired with his eyes staring from a stony face. "My brother, does he know something?" Sabeeka wondered. She knew how it angered him that Abu Fahad had rented the house next door to strangers, and bachelors. He was looking at Dalal, regretfully. "Did she tell him? He will hate me forever. He will not forgive me." He left the room.

Her sister sat by her feet like a small cat. Her mother touched her hot forehead with a hand that still had traces of flour on it. It stung her like bread hot out of the oven. It scorched her heart. From now on she would not feel the heat of the oven.

* * *

Maher. Maher was smiling his radiant smile for her. He came closer to her and kissed her fevered forehead. He raised his head and quietly withdrew. How did he enter? How did he dare to do it? How was he able to penetrate all these barriers? Maybe she had slept and waked. She always dreamed of him. It is love, love. . . .

Her eyes glimmered with a marvelous light. Her face relaxed, she smiled, and her gaze wandered away.

Her mother remembered her own childhood before she married Sabeeka's father. She was a young girl bringing water from the well with an old bucket. She could drink from it but was afraid of the bottom of the well. There was nothing there but darkness. It was deep and mysterious. . . . Then she heard a cry.

Maher knew what happened. The roots of life had died. The door to love was closed forever. Shivering fingers closed the eyelids of loving eyes.

Notes

1. The first words uttered to babies and the last words said to the dying, this expression is used in many different circumstances. In this case it is intended to give protection against illness.

2. Although education is not compulsory in Saudi Arabia, it is not common to take girls out of school. Most girls are encouraged to attend classes and graduate from high school.

3. Muslims are required to make the *hajj* or pilgrimage to Mecca once in their lives if they can afford it. Special companies organize travel arrangements to the holy city and provide guides who lead pilgrims through the rites.

4. Ideally, Saudis marry from within the extended family. Most marriages are arranged by the parents, with the preferred marriage between a young woman and her patrilateral parallel cousin (*ibn amm*). To marry a stranger, whose family is unknown to the parents, is rare.

5. An Arab sailing vessel.

The Game

Sarah Buhaymid

Having a "good time" is, of course, not the "love" that a thoughtful woman wants; she requires commitment, since the rule of the game of casual love is neglect.
—Editors

She turned off the lights in her room and touched the wall with her hand to keep from bumping into the furniture. In this darkness the telephone rang from the corner of the room. It rang and rang, begging to be picked up. Yes, it was trying, insistently, to awaken her emotions in this darkness. But Norah left it moaning and crying. She would not pick it up.

He knew it was the right hour to touch her with the well-chosen words that always crept swiftly into her heart, rendering her unable to resist. He always chose the right time; he knew her movements in the house, and knew the hour when everyone else was resting. She imagined him sitting on the floor near the recorder that played sweet tunes while his lips whispered the most romantic words.

No, a thousand times no! She would not give him another chance to mock her. She would stop him. She hated the long waiting, and his obvious procrastination. He was merely playing an amusing game with her, as spoiled youngsters play. If he really loved her and intended to get involved with her, he would have come forward and formally asked her family for her hand. There was nothing to stop him from doing that.

* * *

Their first meeting had been in a bookstore. She had been searching for books that she needed when she felt a pair of eyes watching her closely. Instantly she veiled her face. She didn't even turn around, for she was a serious girl—not that other type. She dropped the book she was examining and left the store.

The next day she returned to the bookstore to buy what she needed and was surprised again. The same man was now standing where she had stood, examining the books she had looked at yesterday. As she came into the store, he looked up and smiled. Then he surrendered "her place" to her and went out.

Days passed; then she saw a girlfriend walking down the street with a young man. It was the same young man she'd seen in the bookstore. What a surprise! Norah laughed and later asked her girlfriend, "You didn't tell me that you were married, so how could I congratulate you on your happy marriage?"

"May Allah hear your words! But the person you saw me with is my brother, Ahmed. I am still single."

Norah couldn't deny that she was pleased to hear that. Her friend visited her several times and often talked about her brother and how much he liked Norah. Could he phone her? He would like to talk to her before he formally asked her family for her hand.

Thinking it would be all right to do so without her family's permission, Norah told her friend the right time for him to telephone. And since then, he had called her every evening.[1] She found herself enjoying the game—until months had passed, and he began to give excuses for avoiding the commitment of visiting her family to ask for her hand.

She finally realized that he merely wanted amusement. She felt guilty. How would her father or brothers react to hearing about these telephone calls? How would she face them? What excuse could she give them? She *was* guilty and she knew it. She had to stop the game before she reached its humiliating end. Might Allah forgive her for what had already passed! She closed her ears to the phone's ringing. She no longer rushed to pick it up. She wouldn't hear it anymore.

Days, weeks, passed quickly. She did not notice them; she made herself very busy with her school work. Suddenly spring vacation was near, and her brothers were planning a trip. She asked them to take her with them, but they mocked her.

One day she was surprised by a knock on their door; someone handed her a wedding invitation. She opened the envelope with a shivering hand and her heart began to beat fast. She was shocked to read, "This family is honored to invite you to attend their son Ahmed's marriage to Miss Mai. . . ."

The envelope fell from her hand.

Note

1. The telephone has become a popular means of flirting among young men and women in the Kingdom.

I Never Lied

Qumashah al-ᶜUlayyan

This story relates two young girls' experiences with "love" as they are growing up. It dramatizes how much friends influence each other, and also the importance of a loving mother's guidance and help in her daughter's crisis. This girl decides that first love "counts" only within marriage.
—Editors

With tears that he struggled to hide, my father opened the back door of the car for me, and I slipped as I got in. My mother, in the front seat, was trying not to cry. My heart was about to jump out of its place as fear and confusion struggled with craving for the adventure of the unknown.

On the radio Abdulkarim Abdulgadir was singing his famous song, "Farewell to the last night in which we were together . . . farewell to the dearest people." Warm tears rolled down my face, and then my mother's tears and moaning began. "My darling, you are not the first girl who ever married and traveled. All girls marry. . . ."

Then my father shouted at her, "Oh, what's wrong? Suad is going to marry, not to die. You should strengthen her, not undermine it all!" Then he said to me in a trembling voice, "Suad, my dear, as I advised you before, appreciate and respect your husband. He will be your future life. Don't worry, in two years you will come back to Arabia." Then, after a long silence, he said in a grieving tone, "We will bear your farewell and our separation. You will not die. Please, my daughter, be happy, and live your life."

The car stopped in front of the cosmetic salon. My mother

wiped her face as she got out, and so did I. "Don't forget my advice."

I mumbled something covertly as I left the car. My heart was beating like a striking clock as the salon people surrounded me. One started rubbing my legs down, another arranging my hair, another dabbing at my face. Mother was still weeping, and blushing. Her nose looked bigger. I loved her so much—and she loved me most of all her children.

At ten o'clock sharp they had me ready and were admiring their work. In a trembling voice my mother said, "You look extremely beautiful, my dear. The most beautiful bride I have ever seen in my life!"

"Every mother says that to her daughter," the hair stylist said joyfully.

Then we went to the hotel, and my husband arrived.

My husband! This was not the first time I had met him. I saw him when he came to ask my father for my hand, and even spoke to him. As we took the taxi to the airport, he held my hand; with my other hand I waved farewell to my family. Their tears sparkled like sharp lights around me. I wiped my own tears; the beautician had told me not to cry. "Be firm!" So all night I was firmly able to abstain from crying.

We sat beside each other on the flight to London, or course. Other passengers looked at us with curiosity, and maybe admiration. My husband leaned close to me and whispered. Nervously I retreated, but heard him say, "I want to ask you something, and hope you answer me frankly and honestly."

"What?" I whispered.

"Was there no other man in your life before me?"

I had never expected such a question. I was shocked, and began to remember—it was not long ago, only five years. I had asked my mother to let me study with my girl friend Layla. As usual, my mother didn't refuse; I had never abused her trust.

When we became weary of studying, Layla suddenly said, "Suad, let's entertain ourselves with the telephone!"

I knew what she meant, and was afraid; I had never talked to a male stranger in my life, on the telephone, or any other way. "Definite nonsense!" I said. "My mother says that playing with the phone can be dangerous!"

"Ignore the old women's pretenses!" Layla said. She pulled my hand toward the phone. "Come on!" Randomly she dialed a number, and pressed the speaker. I heard what sounded like a young man's voice. Layla spoke to him without fear or shame, and then threw the receiver into my lap. I threw it back. Laughing with ridicule, she said, "You are a cowardly girl—try!"

I took the receiver and trembled with the sweetness of adventure. He asked my name. I hesitated, and Layla signaled "False name!" so I invented one.

"My name is Hisham," he said, and added, "I want to talk to one girl, not two."

Layla winked at me to indicate that I should be the one.

Soon he made me feel that I was flying over clouds, among stars. I was happy.

Twice a day, then, I talked to him: once when I returned from school, again at night when my family slept. I would wait beside the phone until it rang and I heard our secret code; then we talked all night, sometimes until dawn.

I indulged in drinking from that world, neglected my studies, and ignored my friends—even Layla, for fear that she might take my admirer away.

One day Hisham asked when he could see me. I refused, but he insisted. "Let me think about it," I said. I knew I was attractive, but disasters could, would happen if I met him somewhere. Perhaps he just wanted to have a "Western good time," as our tradition didn't allow. "No," I finally said.

"Then I won't call you again," he said.

And he didn't; and the bored, suffering void devastated me. I loved him, I realized. How I missed his voice!

After two weeks I called him, and cried. And he repeated his request. I explained my fears. "Give me your photograph, then," he said. I spent the whole night choosing the best I had.

As we planned, he parked his car near my school—not too near—and I passed by casually, dropping the picture through the window.

That night he called to tell me the most pleasant loving phrases, such as, "I have never seen a girl so beautiful. I dreamed of our wedding, and how our wedding night would be."

A few days later he asked again to see me. "You have the photo," I said. "Isn't that enough? Look at it until your curiosity is satisfied."

"I want to see you!" he insisted. "It is necessary. I will wait in the same place."

"Hisham, are you crazy? I am sorry, I cannot!"

"Then I will use the picture to make you sorry!" he threatened.

At that moment I realized that he knew nothing of love except words.

I didn't know what to do with his threat, or with my grief, so I visited Layla and told her everything. "Why not?" she suggested. "Meet him! He might want to marry you."

Shocked, I couldn't even respond to her. I went to my kind-hearted mother, cried on her shoulder, and told her everything. She hugged me and said, "Let me deal with him. Call him."

"Greetings! So finally you've agreed?" he said eagerly. "When will I see you?"

Then my mother took the phone: "We will be honored to see you in our home, Master Hisham. When will you come?"

He hung up, and I never heard his voice again.

The bitter experience taught me many lessons, but I cane out of it stronger and better than the previous Suad. I stayed away from Layla, too. Some years passed, and I almost forgot it.

But now, here was my husband asking me this question on my very first day with him. I would not lie to him. But the Hisham experience was not one of true love. And Hisham was not truly a man. Therefore, I could confidently answer my husband, who was eagerly waiting for my response.

I looked into his eyes and whispered, "Never. There was no man in my life before you. You are the first, and the last as well."

He smiled happily, and I leaned toward him and smiled at him.

Take Me with You

Najat Khayyat

When Maher leaves for the oil fields, Suha is distraught with loneliness, then grief. This story explores whether she will learn to love again.
—Editors

"Take me with you. I can't bear life without you, take me with you, love. Don't leave me here for loneliness to eat me and fuel my doubts."

But Maher snuffed the last hope on her lips and whispered, "Love, calm down. I'll be back soon." But a tear gave him away as it wandered down his cheek. He tried to control his emotions by forcing words through his mouth: "The hot sun and sand storms would make life very harsh for you in a tent with nothing to protect it in the desert."

Suha interrupted him: "I would go anywhere with you. All I care about is being with you, to feel your presence by your voice, your motion, your smell. The rough desert life will not seem so harsh when I'm with you. The drops of sweat on your brow will call my hand to wipe them. . . . Your burning thirst will await a glass of cold lemonade that I'll prepare for you. These small things will fill my mind so I'll feel nothing but my need for you and yours for me. Please don't condemn me to live here by myself, to prepare food alone and live for myself alone; it will be too horrible to bear. I can't bear counting the hours and minutes until the postman brings a letter from you. Maher, I can't stand that."

Her eyes were full of tears. Maher tried to convince her: "My love, don't be childish. Your presence will only hinder and confuse me. My work is very sensitive and requires concentration. Even though I need you near me, it is enough for me to know that you are safe and far from danger. I'll write whenever I can. I'll be back in a month to find you eagerly waiting for me to fill me with happiness."

He embraced her tightly.

* * *

Maher left to search for oil at the bottom of the earth. Huge drills cut through the soft waves of sand in the chest of the giving land. The drills pumped up and down regularly. The sun sent its burning rays down on the workers. They were in full motion, coming and going, watching everything. All seemed normal.

Maher sat in his small tent examining a specimen from the dirty and dark-colored stones under the microscope. What he saw made him began to sweat. He rushed to the Jeep and drove away. The world spun in his eyes, fire ran in his veins, and his head was ready to explode. At the site, the huge drills were doing their job as usual. Maher stopped, descended quickly from the Jeep, and flew about madly searching for the European expert responsible for supervising the big machines.

With eyes shining hot as noon, Maher asked one of the workers, "Saad, where is the expert?"

"He is in his tent, Sayyid Maher. It is break time."

Maher cursed wildly: "Let the break go to hell! We're in great danger—tell them to stop the machines quickly! This area is made of tough coal and the friction could produce explosion."

The American engineer answered coldly: "We can't stop the machines without an order from the expert."

"The expert, where is the expert?" he kept muttering madly. "The expert, Allah's curse on the expert!"

He ran to the Jeep and started driving toward the expert's tent. Then everything changed to horror, to Judgment Day. The drills exploded and their crashing echoed from the mountains. Red-hot chunks of iron flew in every direction, flames of fire grew and moved upward, dancing the dances of the victorious demon who had been unleashed. Ditches shredded the land. The blood of the workers soaked into the sands. Maher was among them, and with his blood, under the hot sun, he wrote, "Good-bye, my love. Good-bye, Suha."

* * *

Another big wound, too big, was bleeding inside Suha. She repeated, "Why, Maher, why didn't you take me with you?"

Painful, crushing hours passed. Every small thing in her home spoke intimately and sadly about Maher. Things ran after her to cut into her with the whip of memories.

This is the vase where Maher put flowers just hours before he left. The dry flowers weep for the kind hand that put them there. This sofa, how often did it witness their happiness, how often did they sit in it comfortably?

Maher's shorts, toothbrush, sandals, pillow, his half-used perfume, all awaited his return from the fiery desert. This small golden ring was the latest memory. When they recovered his body, they sent her the ring.

Everything shouted, wept, and cried, telling the story of the great love that had joined them together.

* * *

Days passed slowly and dully. Life's pictures changed, past memories paled, objects stopped shouting their stories. Now they told their story more quietly. Maher's pillow, which used to witness Suha's tears every night, was dry. His chair was replaced by another; the vase fell down one day and broke into pieces. His clothes were stored away and eventually even the big wound became but a heap of memories covered by ashes of forgetfulness.

Life ran its natural course. Suha loved again and enjoyed a new husband. His things found their place in her heart and the image of her new love replaced the image of Maher in her eyes.

One day when she and Fareed were having a picnic in the desert, their car broke down in an area where there were scattered pieces of iron, broken rudiments burned by the sun.

Suha looked around. Everything was silent in this lifeless desert. She asked her husband, "What is this place? Do I see something burned over there, is it black ash on the sand?"

Busy fixing the car, Fareed answered absentmindedly, "Habeebti, my love, these are the remains of machines that exploded years ago during the search for oil."

She murmured to herself: "Maher!"

A gentle tear wandered down her cheek, but she did not see the big red wound Maher's blood had written on the chest of the land: "Good-bye, my love. Good-bye, Suha."

PART FOUR
Memories

Burqan's Ghost

Nurah al-Ghamdi

This story dramatizes a village's beliefs about spirits and ghosts. Its theme is the necessity for justice; until it prevails, the village cannot prosper and a dead man's spirit cannot rest in peace.

—*Editors*

"From here, men, we will take the path that's close to the deserted well. It's better and shorter."

"Do you think we'll be able to finish our work tonight?"

"Either come with us or go back, do whatever you like!" a worried voice responded loudly.

"Please, don't misunderstand me. As you know, this is not an easy thing to do."

"I know that, but don't you see all this destruction?"

"Do you really think he is the one who did it?"

"Who else? Look how the palm trees in the grove are flattened to the ground. Look at those holes and furrows where water seeps out to the open desert. Look how the water pools are polluted each night with sand and dirt. Even the water pumps are damaged, despite their concrete covers. Don't you see?"

The flapping of the owl's wings[1] woke the other birds as he flew over the haystack and sometimes clapped on the fronds. The steps were coming closer. Another sound hissed from the bottom of the cliff that overlooked the graveyard next to the deserted well. It passed the dry-frond fence that surrounded the date farms, and became louder to the men hiding behind the haystack. It was the same sound they heard every night, the choked moaning that sometimes turned into sighs and then stifled cries that were wildest and strongest next to the deserted well. Each night these cries crumbled the walls a little more, and as stones fell down, the dust and the rotten smell rose and spread.

Ahmed, the youngest of the men, covered his nose with his turban and whispered, "The village sheikh was right. Last night he was saying that he heard him personally—and he told us this hoarsely, with sweat running down his face. He said that the sheep had run terrified from the pens. Even the watchdogs—those still alive—bark louder when they hear this sound at night. It *is* a ghost, and it threatens our village."

"Perhaps a wild animal?" suggested Asmar.

"But the sheikh confirmed that it is a ghost," Ahmed continued, "and I also say that it is a ghost. An animal couldn't do what it has done, no matter how big it is. Didn't you see the yard of the prayer bead shop? The window was broken, which made the shop keeper give some of his beads away. A sad good deed, for he is very poor. Oh, the stench, and the dust!"

A crash near the haystack scattered dates near the men's feet. Ahmed picked up some dates and chewed emphatically.

"Where are they now, I wonder," Ajooz murmured.

"Who?" Asmar asked.

"My wife and children. She left the village a couple of days ago. She said she can't live in a village full of ghosts. I feel so lonely now."

His friend laughed. "Just your wife? A lot of people ran away. Drink some of this water. Soon your family will come back."

"Pass it to me. Oh, what a rotten smell! It makes me want to vomit. It's not just the smell of the well, but the dead sheep, too. Many have strange diseases, and some have died suddenly. And the crops in this valley are all wasted, even the grains." Sadly he struck his hand.

"We all know that. Just drink now, drink!" said Asmar. He extended his hand to Ahmed. "Can you rub it a bit? It hurts."

"What from?"

"Bandaging the leg of the sheikh's donkey. He strained his tendon really badly. He's a big animal, and struggled hard." In a low voice he continued, "The air is cold tonight. Yes, yes. . . ."

The silence that followed was soon disturbed by the rustling of the tamarisk trees that surrounded the farms, the rustling language known to all villagers. Sometimes it gave its listeners a sense of longing. Sometimes it awakened nervousness and tension, especially when it foretold a cold storm at the time that seeds erupt from the heart of the palm.

"Are you sure," Asmar asked, "of what the blind old woman said? She talked about it very secretly. Perhaps she was frightened."

"Hush!" The moaning had returned, piercing the night. This time it came from the graveyard. Oh, if only the village could be moved farther from the graveyard!

The question returned. "Is it true what the old woman said?"

"We have to accept what she said as true. Or we would not have come out tonight."

With her cane the old blind woman had struck every place where the ghost's steps had touched. "The ghost comes out every night," she had said. "I recognized his voice. But how can a dead person come back to life? He died five months ago!" The old woman had insisted to the sheikh that it was Burqan's ghost that walked through the farms and the sleeping village each night. The sheikh, with some others, had gone to the graveyard, and they found that only part of Burqan's grave had dirt in it.

Then Ajooz said, "Burqan's soul won't rest until someone goes to him and asks him what he wants."

The three men moved together toward the meeting place, using the canal as their path. They left the graveyard and the haystack behind them.

"Oh, Allah! The old man's canal has changed its course," exclaimed Asmar, wiping sweat with his sleeve. "I'm hot just thinking of poor Burqan, even though the wind is cool." He led the others, searching for a path free of deadfall and thorns. From time to time he heard their warnings:

"Careful, the thorn bush is in front of you . . . move away from that ditch. . . ." Despite the dangers, he was occupied by grief for his daughter. He had awakened to the sound of her moaning several days ago, and discovered that she had suddenly been paralyzed.

When Asmar tripped on a stone covered by slippery sand, the moaning returned, louder. Clouds of dust flew in the sky, and the dry fronds creaked again.

Ajooz asked, "Is the prayer bead seller late?"

Ahmed: "He is probably on his way."

They turned toward a winding road edged with trees and old ruins, taking the path to the new mosque that the villagers were building as a beacon from a distance. They could see the sleeping village, the quiet adobe houses exactly alike, and the one-story concrete houses with wood roofs. Palms, tamarisks, and *arar* wood fences surrounded every house.

"Stop here. This is it," said Asmar.

As they came to the meeting place, the fourth man, who was waiting, touched his prayer rug and the shawl on his shoulder. He turned toward the silent water pumps and shook his head. The pumps no longer brought life to the night and to the farms; they were quiet.

He remembered the stories told in the village: that Burqan had stolen from many of his neighbors. The only evidence of his innocence was his testimony, given in the presence of the sheikh. Burqan raised his hand and swore, "The boundaries of that man's farm have not changed. They are the same as when he inherited it from his father and grandfather." Everyone knew mornings when a farmer would wake up to find that some land, or a palm, had been stolen by the wicked Burqan. One-quarter of the blind woman's land had been swallowed by Burqan, who lifted the fence between the farms. The fence was made from tamarisk and dry fronds and jute tied with fibers. Between dusk and dawn Burqan would lift the fence a quarter of a meter, and then tirelessly build another. Then, after a month, he would lift another to take a bigger area.

The prayer bead seller groaned, and bent forward to pluck a thorn from his callused foot. He thought of the villagers, who pressed their prayer beads with dry fingers whenever they crossed the narrow path recently made between the farms and the concrete mosque and passed the deserted well from which dust flew every night. It was the villagers' secret garbage dump. Years ago a rumor had spread that the remains of a baby were found there. The men, upset with the women, then forced the village girls to marry before they were twelve and thirteen. He sighed. His own daughter, a victim of that rumor, had died at fourteen while delivering her first child.

He watched the dust fly from the well and heard the moaning become louder; the rotten smell made him grasp the hem of his *thobe* between his teeth so he could run away as fast as he could. Near the edge of the cliff that separated the valley from the graveyard, his feet dove into dry weeds. "Ya Allah! Ya Allah! Save us from this disaster!" he cried as he joined his three friends.

"Finally you came," one of them teased. "We thought you had decided to stay home in fear."

"No, no. I passed by Burqan's wife's house. She gave birth tonight, a baby boy."

"Thanks be to Allah!" "May Allah bless her." "The baby will be good company for her in her lonely life," they responded.

"The old woman is with her. She was crying and pleading with me to do whatever the old woman said. And the strangest thing, my friends, is that when the baby cried, the horrible howls of the ghost responded. The poor widow kept insisting, 'He took some meters from his neighbor's land! More than once he lifted the old woman's fence, too!' That's the fence that starts at the canal that changed its course when Burqan left his grave. Now he digs every night, trying to do something. We have to be sure of what he is doing, and what he wants!"

Even the hut that separated Burqan's farm from his Bedouin neighbors was not his own. It belonged to the Bedouins who came every fall. "I still remember how fast Burqan finished building that wide hut with a high ceiling," one of the men said. "He used a quarter of the neighbors' fronds, pulled out the trunks of fruit-bearing palms, cut ten tamarisks that surrounded his house, and put five men to work making palm-fiber ropes. Strangely, when the Bedouins came back they confronted his action with silence and just prayed, 'Ya Allah, return our wealth if it is rightfully ours!' "

The ghost was beating the palm trunk again. Burqan used to sleep soundly when he had been alive. In the mornings, his servants would race to fulfill his wishes in return for a poor meal. No one thought his destiny would be so ugly.

"He frightens my children. They can't sleep except between me and their mother."

"Your children aren't the only ones," said Asmar.

"The village squares are deserted, the doors are closed, and the alleys are empty of children's laughter. People threaten their children with the ghost if they don't eat, so my neighbor's children, who always grieved their father by not eating, have become voracious."

"These disasters are nothing compared to my daughter's paralysis," said Asmar.

The prayer bead seller stood in the middle of the group, reading charms and drinking water that the village sheikh had blessed with Quranic verses. Then he began taking his clothes off piece by piece.

"Where are the special herbs?" he asked.

Ahmed came forward and began to rub his naked brown body with leaves from the sidr tree and spray him with lotus and water. After that he painted him with sandalwood oil mixed with amber and rosewater that one of them had brought from a long and tiring trip to Taif.

"Are you all right?" Ahmed asked.

The old woman had directed, "It must be a man with a strong heart who has the courage to enter the graveyard at night and talk to the dead."

The prayer bead seller tightened his white shawl over the lower part of his body and laughed, "If I don't do this, Burqan will keep roaming around the village and that rotten smell will keep coming from the bottom of the well. Poor dead man. Pray that Allah helps me. Where is the gum?"[2]

Asmar handed him a big chunk to chew. They walked in the darkness to the graveyard.

The moaning, the owls, and the dust had quieted. The men stopped at the entrance. The prayer bead seller turned to face the others and began walking backward toward the graves.

"Careful, don't look behind you!" Asmar warned.

Step by step he walked firmly, his back to the grave. A new, unfamiliar smell filled the men's noses, and then a loud howl from deep inside the grave tore the silence of the night. The watchers retreated. They lifted their heads up and then down, and one turned in a full circle. A cold night wind of smoke and howling blew across their faces. Ajooz saw something crawling over the weeds. "Look, a scorpion!" he warned. "Perhaps a soul has changed into this scorpion!" But the cane was faster.

Another howl tore the night, and then another, not so loud, then a fainter third and fourth, then silence.

"Our friend should have left the tomb by now. He is late. Maybe we'd better go."

"Wait—here he comes,"
And they all shouted, "Allahu akbar! Allah is great!"
The prayer bead seller fell at their feet and began to vomit.
"Did you talk to him?"

"Yes, yes, I talked to Burqan. He repeated exactly what his wife said. He pleaded with me. Burqan begged! 'Please,' he said, 'return to its owner every piece of land that I have taken from anyone! And return the fences to their original places! Please! Let me rest!' "

The youngest of the men bent over him and said, "Describe him!"

"I talked to him with my back to the tomb, stupid! If I'd looked at him, he couldn't have talked. Perhaps you forgot. But do not worry, my friend, Burqan is quiet now. He gave me his message. And as tomorrow's sun rises, I will tell it to the people of the village. Come along, friends. Hayya, ya rifaaq."

"Come along, friends." In Burqan's village or any of the nearby villages, "Hayya, ya rifaaq" is a familiar phrase used by anyone who wants to accomplish a significant task. It began the reorganization of the village. The farm boundaries were corrected. Stone and cement canals were built to irrigate the farms; the water was now clean enough to refresh any passerby. And a passerby could rest on a hill surrounded by a circle of beautiful and fragrant wild flowers. If he asked about the secret of this happy place amid the date farms, he was told it was the location of an old deserted well.

Today, whoever passes this beautiful area in the southern region will notice a prosperous town with a big dam. The town gives a sense of organized beauty: quiet, flowered, inhabited by people who do not close their doors to visitors. Carrying flowers or torches, they come out calling, "Come along, friends. Hayya, ya rifaaq."

Notes

1. In Saudi Arabia owls are thought to bring bad luck.
2. Lubaan is chewing gum derived from tree sap.

The Madman

Jamilah Fatani

In an unlettered and narrow-minded village, a scholar can easily be labeled "mad" because he behaves so differently. The narrator, a young girl, is impressed by his vast knowledge and his friendliness. Yet even she is swayed by the ignorant mob, which rejects him.

—*Editors*

She heard them talking about him, Ustadh Saeed, the scholar. "He knows many things." "He sails through each and every field of knowledge." "He is a scholar in religion, literature, politics, medicine, and even in astronomy," and many other sciences, too. More than Ruqayyah could count, or even know their meanings.

She liked his manner of speaking. He spoke with great and strange elegance, waving his hands in harmony with the music of his words. He spoke only classical Arabic and often recited *hadiths* and quranic verses. Often he beautified his speech with classical poetry.

He was a handsome man who always looked dignified. The people of the quarter were used to seeing him carrying books under his arms, or if there were many, against his chest, holding them in both hands. Old and young would often stop him to ask about this problem or that subject; he would answer confidently yet humbly, offering answers that showed his wide breadth of knowledge.

Ruqayyah was a small child, not ten years old. She lived midway between the top and the bottom of the mountain and enjoyed watching him make his way to his house on the top of the high mountain. Often she would stop playing with her friends and toys to watch his balanced steps, his manner of speaking, and the people's respect for him. He was the only one they called "Ustadh," Learned One.

Why, she wondered, did he always carry books? Why did he read them? No one else owned so many books or kept their company to such an extent that they became part of him. Many questions crowded her mind.

"Ustadh Saeed!" she called.

When he saw her, he gave her an absent glance, but she felt in it some kind of strange sadness, something in him that she could not discover. Were these books the secret of his sadness? She quickly refused that idea.

Why did he always carry books? He lived with them more than he lived with his family, people said. He cared so much for them that he even protected them from the smallest speck of dust or drop of rain. Often she would see him running with his books, sometimes to Uncle Khamees's store, where for many hours he would read without feeling tired or bored. Even when he sat on Sheikh Khidir's bench to talk with people of the quarter, he would eventually move aside to read from his books, or else he would read one newspaper after another for them until they left.

"Yes, Ruqayyah," he said to her. "What is it, my daughter?"

She looked at him and his books and asked him, "Why do they call you Ustadh Saeed? Are you the only *ustadh* in our quarter? Is it because you read these books—is it these books that make you such a great man?"

She realized from his gaze that he was far away, and she kept silent, wondering whether he would answer, whether he was angry, what he was thinking. Often she had watched him while he sat at Uncle Khamees's store or on Sheikh Khidir's bench. His eyes might be fixed on the lantern that hung at the end of the pole, a pole like all the other poles posted along the road that led to his house at the mountain top. Or his eyes might be fixed on the man who, following his donkey, collected the trash from the streets and from the baskets that the young children put outside their houses. The man used to drum a special tune, "Oh, young one, the trash!" which harmonized with his knocking on doors. Ustadh Saeed would watch him and then he would put his face back into his books.

"Listen, ya Ruqayyah . . ."

Ustadh Saeed's words brought her from her images of his strange world.

"These books, ya Ruqayyah, are great things. They reveal to me the secrets of the universe. They teach me things that I could not learn on my own. Do you understand what I am saying? Yes, yes, you do. You are very intelligent. Let these books be your friends, too. Give them your mind and heart, and be assured that one day you'll be a great woman, inshallah."

His words continued and she thought she understood some of them; she responded by nodding her head, until in astonishment she stood watching him walk away.

When she heard people talking about him, later on, they were saying, "Ustadh Saeed has gone mad." "He talks to himself." "He utters words like smoke, words you can't give any meaning to." "He has gone mad. Those books that he reads have made him lose his mind." People began to avoid talking to him, and then people began to avoid even meeting him.

One day when Ruqayyah eagerly called to him, "Ustadh Saeed!" one of her friends pulled her aside and whispered fearfully into her ear, "Are you crazy? Do you talk to a madman? Aren't you worried that he may hit you or even kill you?"

"No! I don't believe that. Ustadh Saeed is not mad. It isn't possible. These books are his friends, not his enemy to take away his mind. How can people say that? People just envy him because he is the only *ustadh* among them and because he is great."

But Ustadh Saeed did not answer her greeting. He only watched her for a moment. Ruqayyah murmured in astonishment, "No, no. He can't be mad. No!"

Then children began to shout at him while running away from him, "Madman! Madman!" And one day she saw him stop, put his books down, and throw stones at them. Then some children began pelting him with stones and empty cans, and others joined them. Fear churned inside her and unconsciously she shouted, "Madman! Madman!"

His gaze met hers. She turned to run home but her steps fumbled and then he was throwing a stone at her. She ran until she could close her door behind her. She gasped in pain. When she removed her hand from her head, it was bloody. She was terrified.

"What happened?" her anxious mother questioned.

"Oh, I fell down. I tripped on a rock; I hurt myself," was all she said. She did not know why she lied.

It began to rain heavily; the quarter was immersed in the silence of the rain. All the stores shut their wooden and metal doors, and smoke rose through the wooden *mashribiyyat*, the shutters of the crowded houses.

She saw him coming down from the mountain. He seemed to be breathing in the rain's smell, and silence, and sadness. Her steps led her outside. The sky was bidding farewell to the last breath of the day. The threads of darkness were mixing with the colors of the rainbow, and the smell of rain with the cool breeze.

She shuddered and felt the cold penetrating deep into her flesh. She had not put on her coat; she had been afraid he would walk so fast that she would miss him. She felt her head throbbing, tried to swallow her pain, and wiped her tears.

Then she felt strong hands grab her shoulders and shake her body.

"Even you, Ruqayyah, call me mad? Even you. Am I a madman?"

She was terrified. Did his glaring eyes bear a look of madness? Or was it the glare of a wounded man who wanted revenge? She stared into his face. She was unable to catch her breath.

"Yes, no, never . . . never," she murmured. She wanted to run, but felt as if the mud in the street were glue.

He closed his eyes, and then he removed his hands from her shoulders. Then she saw the tears come down his face. When he opened his eyes his hating look, his mad look was gone. Now he looked grieved.

"No, Ustadh Saeed," she said. "By Allah, you are not mad, not mad. Those who call you mad are crazy, not you."

"You say that because you're afraid of me."

"No. By Allah, no. I'm not afraid of you! Otherwise, why did I come out alone to see you, if I were afraid of you! I came out to tell you that I am sorry, Ustadh. Please forgive me."

"I do not know why these people hurt me, while I've only loved them and never hurt any one of them. Why do they call me mad?"

"They envy you and resent you! You are a great man, and they can't think like you, talk like you, or read like you!"

He nodded. "Can you tell that to my wife, and to the people of the quarter?" The tears in his eyes smiled. "You may be the only one who believes that I am not mad—but they will not hear you or believe you. When you grow up, Ruqayyah, write my story. Do not forget to write my story. I will read it, inshallah, from the unknown place."

The quiet absorbed the last of his whispers and he ruffled her hair. "Good-bye," he said. Darkness embraced him and his quiet steps as he carried his heavy load of books.

The next morning the people of the quarter were whispering, "The madman has left. Ustadh Saeed did not sleep in his house last night. He took most of his books and went away."

He left a small piece of paper for his wife. A literate man of the quarter read it to her and to the others: "I left to search for a heart that is full of love and open to thought."

His wife opened her mouth widely. Then she and the other people said, "Oh, he *is* mad."

One Thousand Braids and a Governess

Raja' ͨAlim

Traditional myths, the Arabian Nights, and other nostalgic themes shift with daily realities in this story to enhance the narrator's self-awareness and understanding.
—Editors

Qahramaana, my new governess, came into the house. My father brought her at a time when my hair was becoming longer and longer and getting a silver hue to it.

When the governess held my braids, she saw all the mystery in them. She murmured and dressed them with a golden oil, while an infinite number of creatures were humming inside my head. I raised my eyes and found Qahramaana smiling strangely. It was as if they had spoken to her and she had heard the prophecy. She rejoiced and the strands of my hair lay all over my shoulders.

* * *

The 1000th night/Twelve o'clock
"What about the kings from days of old? Yazdajer and Kissra? And what about the royal court filled with petitioners?" I asked Qahramaana.

And Qahramaana shook her head. She did not start to tell a story. This was her 1000th night and she did not tell me a story.

"Could one be a governess and be mute?" I jokingly asked my closed window. We hid from my father that she was mute because I liked being with her while my father wanted me to sleep.

* * *

The 1001st night/Midnight

"One knock, two knocks, three," she was counting. This was the first time that Qahramaana spoke. The knocking on the wall has always been there; this sound that we never thought of reading drew an expression of fear on her face. She grimaced and listened, three knocks, two knocks, one.... She untied my braids. She spread the hair around me and stared into it for a while. Then stretched her long fingers, which looked like my father's cane, and lifted up a strand of hair to start on my first braid. When she bent the strand, a miniature jinn[1] the size of Tom Thumb emerged, but she blocked his passage with another strand of hair.

He bowed and said, "I am your slave, waiting to hear your orders."

"Can you make me jump light as a gazelle?" asked a man who suddenly appeared between Qahramaana's fingers. He was the house doctor. His fame and magic sword preceded him; he had crossed valleys and rough roads, and the seven seas of knowledge had surrendered to him. The only thing he owned was his sword. He was bored with wearisome journeys, and word of his reputation had come to us. My father had skin ulcerations that had begun to bleed. My father wanted him, and so the man with the famous sword came to us. He lit matches and showed us, on the blade of his sword, jinn that were busily moving about like ants seeking to enter my father's bones. Everyone who saw this began to scratch. I did not attend the treatment session. The condition was to isolate my father, the jinn, the sword, and loneliness. The sword was heated until it turned red, then it was pressed on the ulcers. The room filled with clouds of smoke and the smell of burning human flesh. My father walked with these brands on him and the house crows slept even though they were at war with each other. The servants whispered to one another that my father should have died from this, and yet he lives. Qahramaana was reading.

My father rewarded the physician by taking him into his private group. All my father's men wore a certain kind of iron shoes. The physician's feet were bare, flat, and pointed straight out. They looked like mud spots close to a tree. How those feet fascinated me and the servants! Happily, the physician put on the iron shoes and became part of my father's group. He began to strut slowly like a peacock, while others carried his famous sword for him. When his legs and body thickened like cement to his neck, my father appointed followers to carry him. He loved my father very much, so much that he even gave up strutting like a peacock. The servants gossiped, "It is the revenge of the seven seas when they are deserted."

"Can you make me jump light as a gazelle?" shouted the physician. The miniature jinn promised to bring him a gazelle instantly. But Qahramaana and I reached the middle of the braid and found no gazelle. Instead of the gazelle, the jinn revealed to us a secret door, a door that even my father did not know about. They said that once my father thought of running away, but then he discovered a talisman. He relaxed and gave up those mad thoughts, and the door stayed closed. The number of people around my father increased, and so he became more determined not to become mad. Now the jinn volunteered to reveal the secret of the talisman.

"After the sun has risen seven times, stand facing the door and only the door. And then with your bare hands and determination, cut off the iron legs and start to run. If your will is strong enough, the legs of a gazelle will carry you and you will be free."

"And what if my will is not strong enough?" shouted the physician. "I do not want to go out without my shoes. My feet are dried out by the cold when I don't wear them."

The jinn dissolved into dust in the silver of my first braid.

* * *

It was twelve o'clock on the 1003rd night.
One knock . . . two knocks.
My Qahramaana took a third strand, braided it, and at exactly twelve o'clock a spray from the fountain was carried into the air. Lightly, Qahramaana's fingers moved to twist my hair around the bars, the bars that circled around the inner courtyard and the courtyard that circled around the fountain. The fountain moved upward over my braid and the cracks in the faces of my father's men. They were not thirsty. The servants moved around the men and the fountain. My handmaiden was caught with silver hands. It was the moon, she was

stretching her arms through the bars to the moon that reflects on the fountain. I envied her. They whipped her, and her arms were thrown into the fountain; Romzan, my father's chief advisor, told him to destroy the fountain. They poured into it thousands of pebbles, but water continued to ooze out. When they finished with the pebbles, water had once again begun to climb into the air inch by inch.

Romzan, who had over a thousand tricks up his sleeve, said, "The glass prison is slowly withering. The medicine is that the illusion inside should wither." So they added to the bars a shawl of glass.

* * *

It was the 1060th night at twelve o'clock and the moon was shining. I begged Qahramaana to teach me polemics. I frowned and listened. Oh! Here was the strange smile on her face once again. There was knocking on all the walls. My hand trembled as she took a section of hair, dividing it into three pieces for braiding.

"There is a man outside, knocking. The man who is knocking wants to rule. Why are you so frightened, my daughter?"

Qahramaana's fingers reached for my trembling shoulders.

"But my father is the only master in this house."

She looked at me again with her strange smile. I was shivering all over. Through the locks came the sound of knocking. Qahramaana's voice came through clearly, telling me about the speech of birds while my fingers ran over a strand of hair interwoven over the peacock.

"I have been told, oh beautiful one, that the wind brought a peacock to your father's house. The peacock and his hen stayed in a tree at night because they were afraid of a monster. They woke up early each morning to search secretly for food until the wind brought them a duck, a donkey, and the venerable horse. They all complained of a dream. The dream was a warning from the humans. And here, when they were unable to do anything and full of fright, they went to the yellow lion cub who lived in a cave at a nearby mountain. When the cub saw their fear, it decided to kill them."

She wove my braid in and out, as if she were spinning the walls of our house.

One knock . . . two knocks . . . ten. . . .

The knocking was now coming out of my braid. I opened an imaginary door. My father was slim, carrying carpenter's tools and nailing cages together. The first one to enter the cage was the cub. My father set him on fire. The rest of the animals entered the cage, touching my father's hammer. Even I entered, wearing peacock feathers. I moved near the edge; my father came in too and closed the door on all of us. My feather touched his skin, I felt his thick hair. Suddenly he was jumping all around us, with the red brands on his back flashing in our faces while we were clapping. My father was tired of the red brands and the famous wise man advised him to wear peacock feathers. They brought a peacock, slaughtered him, and my father dressed in his feathers.

Qahramaana's fingers stretched to start braiding and I begged her not to braid the wild lock of hair. Daughters of nobility have black hearts and Qahramaana pulled my ear. I shook my heart and a black spot bled out of it. I thought to myself, I want revenge for the bird.

*　*　*

And then it was the 1100th night.

Knocking came from all the walls, from all the things, and even from my father's face.

"Is it true that there is a master outside, insisting to come in?"

My Qahramaana angrily braided my 100th braid and did not allow my fingers to touch it.

"The daughters of nobility have their braids done for them and sleep while having tales told to them. . . ."

I suffered from insomnia, neither tales nor fear of my father put me to sleep.

"What does the man outside look like?"

Qahramaana did not answer. I collected some sand that had gathered on the frame of the closed window. I held it in my hand while Qahramaana was braiding my hair. I imagined the face of the man from outside and blew in my hand. Secretly, as Qahramaana was braiding, I hid the man from outside in a strand that was about to be interwoven with another. Qahramaana's eyes glowed and I felt as if I were struck by lightning. Qahramaana was piling my hair around the man from the outside. While she was braiding, the war council was summoned in the presence of my father and the warriors.

"What enemy? There are no enemies here!" I said to Qahramaana, but she told me to be silent.

The plan was executed; jars and vagabonds were brought in. The jars were opened and the army came out. The army was made up of men whose limbs were cut off. Romzan was bidding and my father paid cash. They couldn't walk, they gathered in a pile and followed the directions of the vagabonds. My father ordered them to be stored in the cellar.

"Do you see, there is no war, Qahramaana. There is no kingdom in the whole world except for our house."

A pot fell from the hand of a soldier, which he had hidden under his clothes. My father ordered him to open it. A perfect child came crawling out. The auction over the child took a long time and my father won the bidding. He ordered them to stand the child at attention by the closed door.

"Symbol of victory," he said.

They wrote under his feet, "symbol of the victory." Nine months later, his cries had dried into stone threads, cutting through the air of the house. They had even entered my 100th braid, which was swollen with the sand of his cries.

* * *

The 2100th night

"Tonight you are a bride."

I was bride and all eyes were following me. Romzan was measuring my braids. Everything was swelling—the streets, the walls, all that my eyes fall upon. It was a wedding, and Qahramaana's hand is dribbling colored water coming from the fountain. How did it reach her? I don't know. She washed my face. She dived into my braids and pulled them into one big braid and interwove it around a girl.

I was told that they brought the baby girl from a Bedouin tent the night the master woke up asking for a daughter. They married her the night Romzan awoke asking for a wife.

Suddenly I found myself perfumed and in a strange bedroom. I was frightened. It was the wedding night. My braid was tightening around Romzan's neck. He was dying, my father's right-hand man. It was the wedding, and my braid had killed Romzan. All the streets were closed. I started running; the inner courtyard was filled with bars. The moment I touched them there was the sound of an explosion. I remembered that Qahramaana had left my forelock free.

"There are those who are not captured by tales," I whispered.

I wanted to see my forehead. I looked in the water of the fountain, which was gushing forth from the explosion. I saw in the water Qahramaana's face and my huge braid. She was writhing in pain and staring at us. Everyone in the house was staring at the fountain with its writhing braid. Everyone was staring, and Qahramaana turned into stone. And I was free, ascending into the air inch by inch.

Note

1. Usually called "genie" in the West.

Glossary

abayah	A black outer garment worn by Arab women and adolescent girls whenever they are in public. It covers the body from head to toe.
al-ᶜAsr	The third of the five prayers in the day, the prayer between noon and sundown. Afternoon.
al-Fatiha	The opening chapter of the *Quran,* recited at functions such as marriage or death.
Allah	God.
'ammee	A term of respect used by the young when addressing any unrelated older man. Lit. my paternal uncle.
al-Zuhr	The second of the five prayers in the day, between sunrise and afternoon prayer. Noon.
bint	Girl.
binti	A polite term used by elders when addressing a young girl. Lit. my daughter.
dawafir	(sing. *dafur*) Lit. cooking stove. Metaphorically used to refer to a hard-working person.
dhow	An Arab sailing vessel.
dishdasha	A long white garment worn by Arab men.
fisfis	Small assorted nuts eaten as a snack. The word is created by the sound peanuts, etc. make when being pealed or cracked and eaten.
fitayer	(sing. *fatirah*) A turnover filled with meat, cheese, or spinach.
ghutra	A white scarf worn by men as a headdress.
hadith	A collection of the sayings and actions of the Prophet Mohammad to which Muslims refer for guidance. It is used as a complement to the *Quran.*
hajj	One of the five pillars of Islam; the pilgrimage to Mekkah. Those Muslims who can afford to travel are required to do so once in their lifetime.
ibnee	A polite term used by elders when addressing a young boy. Lit. "my son."

'id	A religious festival. There are two major festivals for Muslims. One of them when completing the month of fasting (Ramadan) and the other at the end of pilgrimage.
igal	A black cord put on the head to hold the ghutrah, the white headdress, in place.
ilhamdillah	Thanks to Allah.
intifadeh	Uprising.
inshallah	If Allah wills. An expression commonly used by Muslims when they give a pledge, or promise, or when they wish or plan for something.
khallas	It's over. Finished.
khawaja	A Westerner.
lubaan	Chewing gum derived from tree sap.
maghrib	The time for the fourth of the five prayers in the day, between afternoon and evening prayer. Sunset. North Africa.
mahram	A close male member of the family who accompanies a female in her travels outside the home.
mashrabiyyat	(sing. *mashrabiyyah*) A projecting oriel window with wooden latticework.
muezzin	A male crier who calls the faithful to prayer five times a day. Before modern-day loudspeakers the caller would climb to the top of the mosque's minaret and sing out in his own voice without the aid of microphones.
murdi	A nanny. Traditionally this woman was also a wet nurse to the child.
Quran	Recitations. The holy book for Muslims said to have been spoken by Allah through Muhammad who recited it, starting in 610. It was written down after his death.
quz	A sand dune.
riyal	A Saudi currency unit. (In 1997, $1.00 = 3.75 riyals.)
salat as-subh	First prayer of the five Muslim prayers. Dawn.
sayyid	A descendant of the prophet. It may also mean "mister."
sheikh	A title for a religious scholar. It is also used for an older man or a respected man in the community.
shukran	Thanks.
sidr	(sing. *sidrah*) A lotus tree.
souq	Marketplace.
surah	A chapter of the *Quran*.

thobe	(also *dishdasha*) The long white robe worn by Arabian men.
umm	Mother of. The mother is usually addressed by her oldest son's name. I.e., Umm Ahmad is the mother of Ahmad.
ustadh	A school teacher. It is also used for a scholar and as a title of respect.
yellah	Let's go.

About the Authors

Amal ᶜAbdul-Hamid (Amal 'Abd al-Ḥamīd) is a pseudonym for Fatimah as-Sa'gh. She grew up in the holy city of Makkah where she received her B.A. in Arabic from Umm al-Qura University. She has published a collection entitled *'Umr az-Zaman* (*From the Age of Time*, 1985) and continues to publish her short stories regularly in local Makkan newspapers.

Raja' ᶜAlim (Rajá' 'Ālim) received her B.A. in English Literature. She works as a tutor for the Center for Training Kindergarten Teachers in Jeddah. She is an active writer of prose and her style—a blend of modern style with traditional themes—is unique among Saudi authors. 'Alim has published several plays, three novels, and a collection of short stories, *Nahr al-Hayawan* (*The Animal River*, 1994). She is the recipient of several prestigious international prizes.

Lamia Baeshen (Lāmīyā' Bā'ashin) was born in Jeddah and studied in the United States, where she received her Ph.D. in English Literature from the University of Arizona. She has served as the chairperson for the Department of European Languages at King Abdulaziz University where she is currently assistant professor. Besides writing short stories, Baeshen has been active translating English works and has compiled a collection of Arabian folk tales entitled *at-Tabat wa an-Nabat*, 1995.

Badriyyah al-Bishir (Badrīyah al-Bashar) was born in Riyadh and received her M.A. in Sociology. She is presently working toward her Ph.D. She has published two collections of short stories: *Nihayat al-Lu 'Bah* (*The End of the Game*, 1992) and *Masa' al-Irbi 'a* (*Wednesday Evening*, 1994). Her novel, *Kharif Sharis* (*Vicious Fall*) is forthcoming.

Sarah Buhaymid (Sārah Būḥaymad) was born in al-Khobar, Saudi Arabia. She studied in Bahrain, then in Lebanon. She returned to the Kingdom where she has worked for the past decade as the principal of a girls' elementary school. She is a poet as well as a short story writer with most of her work appearing in Saudi magazines and newspapers.

Fatimah ad-Dawsari (Fatimah al-Dawsari) is one of the youngest writers in this collection. Her short stories, which have appeared in Saudi newspapers, typically focus on the dilemmas of modern life in the Kingdom.

Mona A. Al-Dokair (Muná al-Dhukayr) obtained her B.A. in History from Cairo University and then studied English at Exeter University. A journalist by training, her literary works include a collection of essays, *Kalimat li al-Akharin* (*Words for Others*, 1981) and a collection of short stories, *Zilal Sihriyyah* (*Magic Shadows*, 1993).

Jamilah Fatani (Jamīlah Faṭānī) graduated with her B.A. in Arabic and is currently working in the Educational Training Department in Riyadh. She has worked as editor for the daily *al-Riyadh*. Both a poet and a journalist, she writes literary and social articles for local newspapers. Fatani has published a collection of short stories entitled *al-Intisar 'ala al-Mustahil* (*Victory over the Impossible*, 1990). Some of her stories have been dramatized for Saudi radio.

Nurah al-Ghamdi (Nūrah al-Ghāmidī) received her B.A. in Arabic at the Girls University College in Riyadh. She started writing short stories at an early age and has published two collections: *'Afwan la Ziltu Ahlum* (*Sorry, I am Still Dreaming*, 1995) and *Tihwa'* (*Part of a Night*, 1997).

Samirah Khashuqji (Samīrah Khāshuqjī) (1940–1986), although born in Saudi Arabia, lived most of her life abroad. She founded a leading women's magazine, *ash-Shaqiyyah*, where she served as editor. Her concern with social problems was reflected in her short stories as well as her involvement with a number of women's associations and charities. She wrote several novels and a number of short story collections. Among these were: *Wadda't Amali* (*Farewell to My Dreams*, 1958), *Dhikrayat Dami'ah* (*Tearful Memories*, 1963), *Wara' ad-Dabab* (*Beyond the Cloud*, 1971), *Qatarat Min ad-Duma* (*Teardrops*, 1979), and *Rihlat al-Hayah* (*A Journey of Life*, 1984).

Najat Khayyat (Najāt Khayyāt), one of the earliest female short story writers in Saudi Arabia, was educated in Beirut. Her work often indicates her abiding interest in women's issues. A journalist, she has written articles on social issues for local newspapers. Aside from her short stories which were published in newspapers, she also has a collection entitled *Makhad as-Samt* (*Pain of Silence*, 1966).

About the Authors

Wafa Munawwar (Wafā' Munawwar) was raised in Mekkah and attended Umm al-Qura University, where she studied art education. Many of her short stories were published in the literary supplement of the daily *al-Riyadh* newspaper. She is also an artist and has exhibited her work in the Kingdom and abroad. Her most recent collection is *ar-Raqs 'ala al-Jirah* (*Dance on Wounds*, 1990).

Khayriyyah as-Saqqaf (Khayrīyah al-Ṣaqqāf), born in Mekkah, obtained a B.A. in Arabic from King Saud University. She continued her education in the United States, where she received her M.A. from the University of Missouri and then her Ph.D. in education from Imam Muhammad bin Saud University in 1988. Besides lecturing, as-Saqqaf has also served as Dean of University College for Girls at King Saud University. An interest in journalism has persisted, and she's an editor for the women's section of the daily newspaper *al-Riyadh*. A number of her short stories were translated into English from her only collection, *An Tubhr Nahw al-Ab'ad* (*Taking Off into the Distance*, 1982).

Sharifah ash-Shamlan (Sharīfah al-Shamlān) was born in southern Iraq, but moved to the Kingdom where she received a B.A. in journalism. Currently, she is the Director General of Women's Social Affairs in the Eastern Province, Ministry of Social Affairs, Dammam. She writes literary articles for newspapers. Two collections of her short stories were published: *Muntaha Al-Hudu'* (*Eternal Tranquility*, 1988), and *Maqati min Haayat* (*Episodes of a Life*, 1991). A third collection, *Wa Ghadan Ya'ti* (*Tomorrow [He] Will Come*), is being prepared for publication.

Qumashah al-cUlayyan (Qumāshah al-'Alīyān) lives in the eastern providence of Saudi Arabia. She is a journalist by training and writes a weekly column for *Kul al-'Usra*, a United Arab Emirates magazine. Aside from her articles, she has published two collections of short stories: *Khata' fi Hayati* (*A Mistake in My Life*, 1992) and *az-Zawjah al-Adhra'* (*The Virgin Wife*, 1992).

Fatimah al-cUtaybi (Fāṭimah al-'Utaybī) received her B.A. in Arabic from the Girls' Education College. She works as a high school teacher in Riyadh. Also an active journalist, al-Utaybi contributes articles for the monthly magazine *al-Majallah al-Arabiyyah*, which is issued in Riyadh. Two collections of her short stores have been published: *Ihtifal bi 'Anni Imra'ah* (*Celebration of Being a Woman*, 1991) and *Dif' Yadayha* (*Her Hand's Warmth*, 1995).

About the Book and Editors

Poignant and thought-provoking, this anthology offers a selection from the past three decades of works by the best-known women writers in Saudi Arabia. The authors' stories of their patriarchal society afford rare insight into the traditional and changing roles, relationships, and expectations of modern Saudi women.

The editors' introductory essay provides background on modern Saudi culture as well as on each of the major themes addressed in the stories. Students of Middle Eastern literature will find this collection both entertaining and enriching.

Abubaker Bagader is professor of sociology at King Abdulaziz University. **Ava M. Heinrichsdorff** is coauthor of *The Fire Goddess.* **Deborah S. Akers** is a doctoral candidate of anthropology at The Ohio State University.